MACMILLAN LITERATURE COLLECTIONS

Animal Stories

edited by Daniel Barber

D1133590

Series Editor: Ceri Jones

Macmillan Education
4 Crinan Street
London N1 9XW
A division of Macmillan Publishers Limited

Companies and representatives throughout the world

ISBN 978-0-230-47029-3

All additional material written by Daniel Barber
The authors have asserted their rights to be identified as the authors of this
work in accordance with the Copyright, Designs and Patents Act 1988.

First published 2015

Designed by Carolyn Gibson

Cover photographs courtesy of Alamy/ClassicStock and
Corbis/O.Alamany & E.Vicens (front)

The authors and publishers are grateful for permission to reprint the following
copyright material: 'My Family and Other Animals' Chapters 2 and 3,
reproduced with Permission of Curtis Brown Group Ltd, London on behalf of
The Estate of Gerald Durrell. Copyright © Gerald Durrell 1956

These materials may contain links for third party websites. We have no control
over, and are not responsible for, the contents of such third party websites.
Please use care when accessing them.

Printed and bound in Thailand

2019   2018   2017   2016   2015
10   9   8   7   6   5   4   3   2   1

Contents

Macmillan Literature Collections

Welcome to the *Macmillan Literature Collections* – a series of advanced-level readers containing original, unsimplified short stories and extracts written by famous classic and modern writers. We hope that these stories will help to ease the transition from graded readers to reading authentic novels.

Each collection in the series includes:

Introduction

- an introduction to the short story
- tips for reading authentic texts in English
- a carefully-chosen selection of classic and modern short stories and extracts.

The stories

Each story is presented in three parts: the introduction and pre-reading support material; the story; and post-reading activities. Each part includes the following sections:

- *About the author* – in-depth information about the author and their work
- *About the story* – information about the story, including background information about setting and cultural references
- *Summary* – a brief summary of the story that does not give away the ending.

Pre-reading activities

- *Key vocabulary* – a chance to look at some of the more difficult vocabulary related to the main themes and style of the story before reading the story
- *Main themes* – a brief discussion of the main themes, with questions to keep in mind as you read.

The story

You will find numbered footnotes in the stories. These explain cultural and historical references, and key words that you will need to understand the text. Many of these footnotes give definitions of words which are very formal, old-fashioned or rarely used in modern English.

You will find more common, useful words and phrases from the stories in the *Glossary* at the end of the book. Words included in the *Glossary* will appear in **bold**.

Post-reading activities

- *Understanding the story* – comprehension questions that will help you make sure you have understood the story
- *Language study* – a section that presents and practises key linguistic and structural features of authentic literary texts (you will find an index of the areas covered at the end of the book)
- *Literary analysis* – discussion questions that guide you to an in-depth appreciation of the story, its structure, its characters and its style. This section will help you develop your analytical skills and is particularly useful if you are studying, or intending to study, literature in the medium of English. Each section includes literary terms with which you may or may not be familiar. For help with these terms visit the Macmillan Readers website at www.macmillanenglish.com/readers. Here you will also find an *Answer key* for all the activities accompanying each story.

In addition, at the end of each book there are:
- suggested *Essay questions*
- a comprehensive *Glossary* highlighting useful vocabulary from each story
- an index for the *Language study* section.

How to use these books

You can use these books in whatever way you want. You may want to start from the beginning and work your way through. You may want to pick and choose. The *Contents* page gives a very brief, one-line introduction to each story to help you decide where to start. You may want to read about the author and the story before you read each one, or you may prefer to read the story first and then find out more about it afterwards. Remember that the stories and the exercises can be challenging, so you may want to spend quite a long time studying each one. The most important thing is to enjoy the collection – to enjoy reading, to enjoy the stories and to enjoy the language that has been used to create them.

Introduction

What is a short story?

A short story is shorter than a novel, but longer than a poem, and is usually between 1,000 and 20,000 words long. It tells a story that can usually be read quite quickly. It often concentrates on one central event; it has a limited number of characters, and takes place within a short space of time.

History of the short story

Stories and storytelling have existed for as long as people have had language. People love and need stories. They help us explain and understand the world. Before people could read or write, storytellers travelled from village to village, telling stories.

The first written stories developed from this storytelling tradition. Two of the best-known examples of early written stories in Europe appeared in the 14th century. Chaucer's *The Canterbury Tales* and Boccaccio's *Decameron* are both based on the same idea: a group of people who are travelling or living together for a short time, agree to tell each other stories. Their individual short stories are presented together as one long story.

The first modern short stories appeared at the beginning of the 19th century. Early examples of short story collections include the *Fairy Tales* (1824–26) of the Brothers Grimm, and Edgar Allan Poe's *Tales of the Grotesque and Arabesque* (1840). In the late 19th century, printed magazines and journals became very popular and more and more short stories were published. By the 20th century most well-known magazines included short stories in every issue and the publishers paid a lot of money for them. In 1952 Ernest Hemingway's short story, *The Old Man and the Sea*, helped sell more than five million copies of the magazine *Life* in just two days.

The short story today

Today, short stories are often published in collections called anthologies. They are usually grouped according to a particular category – by theme, topic, national origin, time, or author. Some newspapers and magazines continue to print individual stories. Many short stories are first published on the Internet, with authors posting them on special interest websites and in online magazines.

Reading authentic literary texts in English

Reading authentic literary texts can be difficult. They may contain grammatical structures you have not studied, or expressions and sayings you are not familiar with. Unlike graded readers, they have not been written for language students. The words have been chosen to create a particular effect, not because they are easy or difficult. But you do not need to understand every word to understand and enjoy the story.

When you are reading in your own language you will often read so quickly that you skip over words, and read for the general effect, rather than the details. Try to do the same when you are reading in English. Remember that stopping to look up every word you don't know slows you down and stops you enjoying the story.

When you are reading authentic short stories, remember:
- It should be a pleasure!
- You should read at your own pace.
- Let the story carry you along – don't worry about looking up every word you don't understand.
- Don't worry about difficult words unless they stop you from understanding the story.
- Try not to use the *Glossary* or a dictionary when you're reading for the first time.

You might want to make a note of words to look up later, especially key words that you see several times (see *Using a Dictionary* on page 9 for more tips on looking up and recording new words). But remember, you can always go back again when you have finished the story. That is the beauty of reading short stories – they are short! You can finish one relatively quickly, especially if you do not worry about understanding every single word; then you can start again at the beginning and take your time to reread difficult passages and look up key words.

Preparing yourself for a story

It is always a good idea to prepare yourself, mentally, before starting a story.
- Look at the title. What does it tell you about the story? What do you expect the story to be about?
- If there is a summary, read it. This will help you follow the story.
- Quickly read the first few paragraphs and answer these questions: Where is it set?

When is it set?

Who is the main character?

– As you read, concentrate on following the gist (the general idea) of the story. You can go back and look at the details later. You can use the questions at the end of the story (see *Understanding the story*) to help you make sure you understand what is happening.

Tips for dealing with difficult passages

Some stories include particularly difficult passages. They are usually descriptive and give background information, or set the scene. They are generally difficult to follow because they are full of specific details. Try to read these passages quickly, understanding what you can, and then continue with the story. Make a note of the passage and come back to it later, when you have finished the whole story.

If, at any time, you are finding it difficult to follow the story, go back to this difficult passage. It may hold the answers to your questions.

Read through the passage again carefully and underline all the unknown words. Try to understand as much as you can from the immediate context and what you now know about the story. Then, look up any remaining words in the *Glossary* at the back of the book, or in your dictionary.

Tips for dealing with difficult words

– Decide if the word (or phrase) is important to the overall message. Read the whole paragraph. Do you understand the general meaning? Yes? Then the word isn't important. Don't worry about it. *Keep reading!*

– If you decide the word is important, see if you can work out its meaning from the context. Is it a verb, a noun or an adjective? Is it positive or negative? What word would you translate it into in your language? Underline it or make a note of it and the page number, but *keep reading*. If it really is an important word, you'll see it again.

– If you keep seeing the same word in the story, and you still can't understand it, look in your monolingual dictionary!

Using a dictionary

Looking up words

Before you look up the word, look at it again in its context. Decide what part of speech it is. Try to guess its meaning from the context. Now look it up in your dictionary. There may be more than one definition given. Decide which one is the most appropriate. If the word is something very specific, e.g. the name of a flower or tree, you may want to use a bilingual dictionary to give you the exact translation.

Let's look at how this works in practice. Look at this short extract and follow the instructions below.

> ... there is a little valley or rather **lap** of land among high hills, which is one of the quietest places in the whole world. A small **brook** glides through it, with just murmur enough to **lull** one to repose*
>
> *literary: *sleep or rest*
> *The Legend of Sleepy Hollow* by Washington Irvine

1 Look at the words in bold and decide what part of speech they are – noun, verb, adjective, etc.
2 Try to guess what it might mean.
3 Look at the extracts below from the *Macmillan English Dictionary for Advanced Learners*. Choose the most appropriate definition.

Words with more than one entry Sometimes the same word belongs to more than one word class: for example, **brook** can be both a noun and a verb. Each word class is shown as a separate entry. The small number at the end of the head-word tells you that a word has more than one entry. **Idioms and fixed expressions** Some words are often used in idioms and fixed expressions. These are shown at the end of the entry, following the small box that says PHRASE. **Words with more than one meaning** Many words have more than one meaning, and each different meaning is shown by a number.	**brook¹** noun a small river **brook²** verb **not brook** – to definitely not allow or accept something **lap¹** noun 1 the top half of your legs above your knees when you sit down 2 one complete turn around a course in a race PHRASE **in the lap of luxury** in very comfortable and expensive conditions **lap²** verb 1 if an animal laps water, it drinks it gently with its tongue **lull¹** noun a quiet period during a very active or violent situation **lull²** verb 1 to make someone feel relaxed and confident so that they are not prepared for something unpleasant to happen: *their report lulled us into a false sense of security* 2 to make someone relaxed enough to go to sleep

Dictionary extracts adapted from the Macmillan English Dictionary 2nd Edition © Macmillan Publishers Limited 2007 *www.macmillandictionary.com*

Keeping a record

When you have looked in your dictionary, decide if the word could be interesting or useful to you. If it is, make a note of it, and write down its definition. Make a note of the sentence where you found it in the story, then write one or two more examples of your own. Only do this for those words you think you will need to use in the future.

Here is an example of how you might record the word *lull*.

'with just murmur enough to <u>lull</u> one to repose'
<u>Lull</u> – to make you feel relaxed enough to go to sleep
e.g. The quiet sound of the waves lulled me to sleep
The mother sang to her baby to lull it to sleep

Literary analysis

The Literary analysis section is written to encourage you to consider the stories in more depth. This will help you to appreciate them better and develop your analytical skills. This section is particularly useful for those students who are studying, or intending to study, literature in the medium of English. Each section includes literary terms with which you may or may not be familiar.

Macmillan Readers website

For more help with understanding these literary terms, and to find Answer keys to all the exercises and activities, visit the Macmillan Readers website at www.macmillanenglish.com/readers. There you will also find a wealth of resources to help your language learning in English, from listening exercises to articles on academic and creative writing.

The Cat that Walked by Himself
by Rudyard Kipling

About the author

During his lifetime, Rudyard Kipling was one of the most popular writers of poetry and fiction in the English language, and he still attracts readers today. He wrote for adults and children. These days he is best known for his children's literature, but his novels and poems for adults are also regarded as literary classics.

Joseph Rudyard Kipling was born in Bombay, India, in 1865. This was during the British Raj, a time in India's history when it was ruled by the British Empire, so many British men and their families lived there. His father was an artist and art teacher in Bombay and his mother was a popular figure in Anglo-Indian society. It was normal for British families in India to send their children to England for their education; Kipling and his younger sister Alice were taken back to live with foster parents in England when they were just five and three years old.

Kipling's foster family were cruel to him and he missed his life in India terribly. Life didn't get much easier for the young boy when, in 1877, he was sent to a boarding school in the south west of England. It was a rough environment and he was bullied by other boys, but despite this, he made some good friends. It was here that his love for books and literature grew, helped by the headmaster, who encouraged him to write. From this point on, Kipling wrote huge numbers of poems, stories and articles. This productivity would last for most of the rest of his life.

At age 16, Kipling failed to get a scholarship to Oxford University and, as his parents couldn't afford to pay the fees, he moved back to India to begin his professional career. His father helped him to get a job as a journalist at a newspaper in Lahore (now in Pakistan), *The Civil and Military Gazette*. His boss gave him lots to do, but Kipling loved writing so much that he not only wrote articles for the paper but produced poems and, later, short stories for it, too.

He worked hard for the seven years that he spent as a young adult in India but he also managed to travel all over India, Pakistan and

Bangladesh. Much of his writing concerns the people and places that he got to know there. In 1886, when he was just 21, Kipling published his first volume of poetry, *Departmental Ditties*, a collection taken from the poems he had printed in the newspaper. Over the next two years, he wrote many short stories, all set in India, which were published in six volumes called the *Indian Railway Stories*.

In 1889 he returned to London, where he already had a reputation as a promising young writer. He married an American, Caroline Balestier, in 1892 and they moved to the USA after their wedding. They lived a healthy life in the countryside and, even though Kipling was not completely happy living in the USA, he had lots of time for writing. It was there that he wrote most of *The Jungle Book* as well as his masterpiece novel, *Kim*. He also became a father; they had two daughters, Josephine and Elsie, and a son, John. Kipling loved reading stories to the children and it was here that he also started writing his *Just So Stories for Little Children*, of which *The Cat that Walked by Himself* is one.

The family moved back to London in 1896. In 1899, the Kiplings experienced tragedy when Rudyard and Josephine, his eldest daughter, both caught pneumonia on a return visit to America. Josephine did not survive the illness. Kipling was deeply affected by this loss. When the *Just So Stories* were published three years later, it is easy to imagine that he had written them for her. The storyteller addresses the reader: 'O my Best Beloved', a reference to his children and specifically Josephine.

In 1907 he was awarded the Nobel Prize for Literature. The prize citation said: 'In consideration of the power of observation, originality of imagination, virility of ideas and remarkable talent for narration which characterize the creations of this world-famous author.' During the First World War (1914–18), Kipling voiced the thoughts and feelings of the nation in his poetry and writings, supporting the war with military and anti-German propaganda. However, the terrible tragedy of this war, in which millions of young men died, meant that many people did not agree with his ideas any more, and through the rest of his life he grew less and less influential in British culture. He died in 1936 aged 70. His ashes are buried in Poet's Corner in Westminster Abbey in London, next to the graves of Charles Dickens and Thomas Hardy.

Nowadays Kipling is probably best known because of the Disney classic cartoon of his stories from his book for children, *The Jungle Book*. The *Just So Stories* is also a popular title on children's bookshelves. He is viewed as one of the main representatives of the British Empire, a period of history that some Britons are still proud of today. Kipling's poem 'If–' has been voted one of the United Kingdom's favourite poems.

About the story

The Cat that Walked by Himself was first published in the magazine *Ladies' Home Journal* in July 1902. In the same year, it was included in a collection of thirteen similar short stories under the title *Just So Stories for Little Children*. Kipling added a poem at the end of each story. He also illustrated the book. Other stories include *How the Camel Got His Hump* and *How the Leopard Got His Spots*. The *Just So Stories* have been printed many times, adapted for television as cartoons and even turned into songs.

Background information

Origin stories

Origin stories are fictional tales which explain how something came to be the way it is and often, why animals are the way that they are. Cultures around the world have always used folk stories to explain the world and its beginnings. Some of the most ancient writing in the world, such as religious texts, include stories about the creation of the world.

Although the *Just So Stories* are only just over a century old, they are among the best-known origin stories. The collection explains, for example, why the leopard is covered in spots and how the kangaroo came to have such long back legs. The title of the collection is a humorous way of saying that the stories are true; if something happens *just so*, it happens in exactly that way.

Domestication

Humans are most familiar with the species of animals that we have domesticated, such as dogs, sheep, horses and cows. These animals have a close relationship with us due to the fact that each of them provides us with something, either food, transportation, labour or protection. However, even though some of these animals have been in human society for thousands of years, we know very little about how they first became domesticated. To begin with, all of these animals were wild. The domestic dog, for example, is descended from the wolf. However, at some point in modern human development they were adopted by humans and these animals became tame and used to living alongside us. Exactly when and how this happened is not clear. It is believed that dogs were domesticated many thousands of years ago, when people hunted animals and moved from place to place more. Cats probably started living with humans much later, only about 12,000 years ago, when people were farming and living in one place. A problem for farmers who stored grains like wheat and corn for long periods was that mice and rats ate the food, so having cats around to catch them would have been an advantage. People may have domesticated cats deliberately in order to catch the mice; another possibility is that cats took advantage of the large numbers of mice and rats around people and invited themselves into people's houses and farms, where they could also enjoy comfortable shelter.

The domestic cat, *Felis catus*, is one of a group of small cats that include the jungle cat of southeast Asia, the European wildcat, the African wildcat and the Arabian sand cat. The domestic cat is probably a descendant of one or more of these. Cats have not changed as much as dogs in the domestication process. There is much less variation in size and shape, for example, and house cats can still survive in the wild when necessary.

Summary

It may help you to know something about what happens in the story before you read it. Don't worry, this summary does not tell you how the story ends!

The story takes place at a time when all the animals were wild, including animals that are nowadays tame, such as the dog and the horse. A man and a woman live in a cave near some woods and when the woman lights a fire to cook food, the smell travels to the wild animals in the woods.

The animals see the fire and smell the food and they are worried that it will hurt them in some way. The dog decides to investigate and asks the cat to come with him, but the cat refuses, so the dog leaves for the cave on his own. The cat decides to quietly follow to see what happens. When he arrives at the cave, the dog is curious to know what smells so good. The woman gives him a piece of meat, but she will only give him more if he agrees to help the man to hunt and to guard the cave. The dog accepts the offer and agrees to be their friend. The cat, who has been listening to their conversation, thinks that the dog is being very foolish and walks away.

The next night, the woman makes some hay by drying some grass in front of the fire. This time the horse decides to investigate. Once again, the cat follows secretly behind. The horse is interested in the grass and asks for some, so the woman makes a bargain with the horse, too. This time, the horse agrees to be the servant of the man and woman, and lets the woman put a piece of rope around his neck. The same thing happens with the cow the following day. She agrees to give her milk to the woman every day in exchange for the hay.

The next day no one goes to the cave, so the cat decides to go on his own. In the cave, he sees the light of the warm fire and smells the milk and wishes to enter, but the woman is not interested in keeping a cat. She has all the animals that she needs. The cat thinks that the other animals are foolish for letting themselves be domesticated but at the same time he is very keen to enjoy some of the comforts of the cave. Is there any way that he can avoid being domesticated but still get what he wants? Or is the woman too clever and wise for him?

Pre-reading activities

Key vocabulary

This section will help you familiarize yourself with some of the more specific vocabulary used in the story. You may want to use it to help you before you start reading, or as a revision exercise after you have finished the story.

Animals in the story: parts of animals

1 **Which of the following body parts of animals are not normally visible on an animal? Why can't you see them?**

> **hide** the skin of an animal, such as a cow, that is used for making leather
> **horns** the hard, pointed parts that usually grow in a pair on the heads of some animals, for example cows or goats
> **mane** the long hair on the neck of a horse or lion
> **marrow** the soft substance inside bones
> **pad** an area of flesh on the bottom of the foot of an animal, such as a cat or dog
> **shoulder blade** one of the two flat bones at the top of your back, near your shoulders

2 **Complete these sentences with the appropriate form of the words in exercise 1.**

1 From the .... of just one of these animals, you can make at least three pairs of shoes.
2 He rode the horse without a saddle, holding onto its long .... with one hand.
3 Now be careful going across the bull's field and remember, if he attacks, watch out for his ....!
4 The animal had not eaten in weeks and you could see its .... standing out quite clearly from its back.
5 The lion gets a sharp piece of wood caught in the .... of its paw and it cannot walk.
6 The x-ray showed a lack of .... in his left leg, which is why it broke so easily.

Physical actions

3 **Match the verbs in bold in the sentences (1–11) below with their definitions (a–k).**

1 All the mothers **cooed** over Harriet's new-born baby.
2 Carrie **slipped** out of class while the others were watching something in the playground.
3 He hurried off, his assistants **trotting** after him.
4 I can't share a room with him. He **strews** his clothes all over the floor.
5 It was Carmen's first time in such high heels and she **stumbled** all the way to the bus stop.
6 Mary tried to **stamp** on the spider with her foot but it ran away.
7 The cat saw the dog coming and **arched** its back in threat.
8 The dogs had a great time **frolicking** on the beach.
9 The girls aren't playing, they're upstairs **plaiting** each other's hair.
10 Vern picked up the hamster but its whiskers **tickled** him and he immediately dropped it.
11 We'd finished eating but Jack kept **gnawing** his chicken bones.

a) form a curved shape
b) speak in a soft and gentle way, such as when you talk to babies
c) play in a happy way with a lot of energy and movement
d) keep biting something
e) twist three long lengths of hair, rope, wool, etc over and under each other to make one single piece. The usual American word is 'braid'
f) go somewhere quickly and quietly without people noticing you or stopping you
g) put your foot down hard and noisily on someone or something
h) spread things around in a careless or untidy way
i) fall, or almost fall, while you are walking or running
j) to move lightly on someone's skin in order to give them a pleasant feeling or to make them laugh
k) walk with short, quick steps so that you are almost running

Main themes

Before you read the story, you may want to think about some of its main themes. The questions will help you think about the story as you are reading it for the first time. There is more discussion of the main themes in the *Literary analysis* section after the story.

Making bargains

A bargain is an agreement in which two people or groups each promise to do something for each other. Bargains are made in the story when the characters agree to help each other in specific ways.

As you read the story, think about the following questions:

a) Who makes bargains and why?
b) Are the bargains equal for both sides?

Wildness

The story is set in the Wet Wild Wood. The characters are described as wild, too, but some are wilder than others.

As you read the story, ask yourself:

a) Are there any benefits to being wild? What are they?
b) Which characters are willing to give up being wild? Why do they do it?
c) What is the opposite of being wild? Is it important in the story?

Fables

A fable is a traditional story, usually about animals, that teaches a moral lesson about right and wrong. Fables can be found in the literature of almost all cultures and languages. *The Cat that Walked by Himself* has a lot in common with traditional fables.

As you read the story, ask yourself:

a) What features makes it feel like a fable?
b) Does the story have a moral lesson to teach or is it simply designed to entertain?

The Cat that Walked by Himself

by Rudyard Kipling

HEAR and attend and listen; for this befell[1] and behappened[2] and became and was, O my Best Beloved, when the Tame animals were wild. The Dog was wild, and the Horse was wild, and the Cow was wild, and the Sheep was wild, and the Pig was wild – as wild as wild could be – and they walked in the Wet Wild Woods by their wild lones[3]. But the wildest of all the wild animals was the Cat. He walked by himself, and all places were alike to him.

Of course the Man was wild too. He was dreadfully wild. He didn't even begin to be tame till he met the Woman, and she told him that she did not like living in his wild ways. She picked out a nice dry Cave, instead of a heap of wet leaves, to lie down in; and she strewed clean sand on the floor; and she lit a nice fire of wood at the back of the Cave; and she hung a dried wild-horse skin, tail-down, across the opening of the Cave; and she said, 'Wipe your feet, dear, when you come in, and now we'll keep house.'

That night, Best Beloved, they ate wild sheep roasted on the hot stones, and flavoured with wild garlic and wild pepper; and wild duck stuffed with wild rice and wild fenugreek[4] and wild coriander; and marrow-bones of wild oxen; and wild cherries, and wild grenadillas[5]. Then the Man went to sleep in front of the fire ever so happy; but the Woman sat up, combing her hair. She took the bone of the shoulder of **mutton** – the big fat blade-bone – and she looked at the wonderful marks on it, and she

1 *literary:* if something unpleasant befalls you, it happens to you
2 to happen. Kipling invented this word for the story (befall + happen)
3 by their lones = by themselves, or alone. Kipling invented the phrase.
4 a plant with white flowers whose seeds are used for flavouring food
5 a type of fruit similar to a passion fruit

threw more wood on the fire, and she made a Magic. She made the First Singing Magic in the world.

Out in the Wet Wild Woods all the wild animals gathered together where they could see the light of the fire a long way off, and they wondered what it meant.

Then Wild Horse stamped with his wild foot and said, 'O my Friends and O my Enemies, why have the Man and the Woman made that great light in that great Cave, and what harm will it do us?'

Wild Dog lifted up his wild nose and smelled the smell of roast mutton, and said, 'I will go up and see and look, and say; for I think it is good. Cat, come with me.'

'Nenni!⁶' said the Cat. 'I am the Cat who walks by himself, and all places are alike to me. I will not come.'

'Then we can never be friends again,' said Wild Dog, and he trotted off to the Cave. But when he had gone a little way the Cat said to himself, 'All places are alike to me. Why should I not go too and see and look and come away at my own liking.' So he slipped after Wild Dog softly, very softly, and hid himself where he could hear everything.

When Wild Dog reached the mouth of the Cave he lifted up the dried horse-skin with his nose and sniffed the beautiful smell of the roast mutton, and the Woman, looking at the blade-bone, heard him, and laughed, and said, 'Here comes the first. Wild Thing out of the Wild Woods, what do you want?'

Wild Dog said, 'O my Enemy and Wife of my Enemy, what is this that smells so good in the Wild Woods?'

Then the Woman picked up a roasted mutton-bone and threw it to Wild Dog, and said, 'Wild Thing out of the Wild Woods, taste and try.' Wild Dog gnawed the bone, and it was more delicious than anything he had ever tasted, and he said, 'O my Enemy and Wife of my Enemy, give me another.'

The Woman said, 'Wild Thing out of the Wild Woods, help my Man to hunt through the day and guard this Cave at night, and I will give you as many roast bones as you need.'

6   an old French word meaning 'no'. Perhaps Kipling thought that it sounds like the noise a cat might make.

'Ah!' said the Cat, listening. 'This is a very wise Woman, but she is not so wise as I am.'

Wild Dog crawled into the Cave and laid his head on the Woman's **lap**, and said, 'O my Friend and Wife of my Friend, I will help Your Man to hunt through the day, and at night I will guard your Cave.'

'Ah!' said the Cat, listening. 'That is a very foolish Dog.' And he went back through the Wet Wild Woods waving his wild tail, and walking by his wild lone. But he never told anybody.

When the Man waked[7] up he said, 'What is Wild Dog doing here?' And the Woman said, 'His name is not Wild Dog any more, but the First Friend, because he will be our friend for always and always and always. Take him with you when you go hunting.'

Next night the Woman cut great green armfuls of fresh grass from the water-meadows[8], and dried it before the fire, so that it smelt like **new-mown** hay, and she sat at the mouth of the Cave and plaited a **halter** out of horse-hide, and she looked at the shoulder of mutton-bone – at the big broad blade-bone – and she made a Magic. She made the Second Singing Magic in the world.

Out in the Wild Woods all the wild animals wondered what had happened to Wild Dog, and at last Wild Horse stamped with his foot and said, 'I will go and see and say why Wild Dog has not returned. Cat, come with me.'

'Nenni!' said the Cat. 'I am the Cat who walks by himself, and all places are alike to me. I will not come.' But **all the same** he followed Wild Horse softly, very softly, and hid himself where he could hear everything.

When the Woman heard Wild Horse tripping and stumbling on his long mane, she laughed and said, 'Here comes the second. Wild Thing out of the Wild Woods what do you want?'

Wild Horse said, 'O my Enemy and Wife of my Enemy, where is Wild Dog?'

7 *old-fashioned*: woke up
8 a field next to a river that fills with water when the river floods

The Woman laughed, and picked up the blade-bone and looked at it, and said, 'Wild Thing out of the Wild Woods, you did not come here for Wild Dog, but **for the sake of** this good grass.'

And Wild Horse, tripping and stumbling on his long mane, said, 'That is true; give it me to eat.'

The Woman said, 'Wild Thing out of the Wild Woods, bend your wild head and wear what I give you, and you shall eat the wonderful grass three times a day.'

'Ah,' said the Cat, listening, 'this is a clever Woman, but she is not so clever as I am.' Wild Horse bent his wild head, and the Woman slipped the plaited hide halter over it, and Wild Horse breathed on the Woman's feet and said, 'O my Mistress, and Wife of my Master, I will be your servant for the sake of the wonderful grass.'

'Ah,' said the Cat, listening, 'that is a very foolish Horse.' And he went back through the Wet Wild Woods, waving his wild tail and walking by his wild lone. But he never told anybody.

When the Man and the Dog came back from hunting, the Man said, 'What is Wild Horse doing here?' And the Woman said, 'His name is not Wild Horse any more, but the First Servant, because he will carry us from place to place for always and always and always. Ride on his back when you go hunting.'

Next day, holding her wild head high that her wild horns should not catch in the wild trees, Wild Cow came up to the Cave, and the Cat followed, and hid himself just the same as before; and everything happened just the same as before; and the Cat said the same things as before, and when Wild Cow had promised to give her milk to the Woman every day in exchange for the wonderful grass, the Cat went back through the Wet Wild Woods waving his wild tail and walking by his wild lone, just the same as before. But he never told anybody. And when the Man and the Horse and the Dog came home from hunting and asked the same questions same as before, the Woman said, 'Her name is not Wild Cow any more, but the Giver of Good Food. She will give us the warm white milk for always and always and always, and I will take care of her while you and the First Friend and the First Servant go hunting.

Next day the Cat waited to see if any other Wild thing would go up to the Cave, but no one moved in the Wet Wild Woods, so the Cat walked there by himself; and he saw the Woman milking the Cow, and he saw the light of the fire in the Cave, and he smelt the smell of the warm white milk.

Cat said, 'O my Enemy and Wife of my Enemy, where did Wild Cow go?'

The Woman laughed and said, 'Wild Thing out of the Wild Woods, go back to the Woods again, for I have braided up my hair, and I have put away the magic blade-bone, and we have no more need of either friends or servants in our Cave.'

Cat said, 'I am not a friend, and I am not a servant. I am the Cat who walks by himself, and I wish to come into your Cave.'

Woman said, 'Then why did you not come with First Friend on the first night?'

Cat grew very angry and said, 'Has Wild Dog told tales of me?'

Then the Woman laughed and said, 'You are the Cat who walks by himself, and all places are alike to you. You are neither a friend nor a servant. You have said it yourself. Go away and walk by yourself in all places alike.'

Then Cat pretended to be sorry and said, 'Must I never come into the Cave? Must I never sit by the warm fire? Must I never drink the warm white milk? You are very wise and very beautiful. You should not be cruel even to a Cat.'

Woman said, 'I knew I was wise, but I did not know I was beautiful. So I will make a bargain with you. If ever I say one word in your **praise** you may come into the Cave.'

'And if you say two words in my praise?' said the Cat.

'I never shall,' said the Woman, 'but if I say two words in your praise, you may sit by the fire in the Cave.'

'And if you say three words?' said the Cat.

'I never shall,' said the Woman, 'but if I say three words in your praise, you may drink the warm white milk three times a day for always and always and always.'

Then the Cat arched his back and said, 'Now let the Curtain at the mouth of the Cave, and the Fire at the back of the Cave, and the Milk-pots that stand beside the Fire, remember what my Enemy and the Wife of my Enemy has said.' And he went away through the Wet Wild Woods waving his wild tail and walking by his wild lone.

That night when the Man and the Horse and the Dog came home from hunting, the Woman did not tell them of the bargain that she had made with the Cat, because she was afraid that they might not like it.

Cat went far and far away and hid himself in the Wet Wild Woods by his wild lone for a long time till the Woman forgot all about him. Only the Bat – the little upside-down Bat – that hung inside the Cave, knew where Cat hid; and every evening Bat would fly to Cat with news of what was happening.

One evening Bat said, 'There is a Baby in the Cave. He is new and pink and fat and small, and the Woman is very fond of him.'

'Ah,' said the Cat, listening, 'but what is the Baby fond of?'

'He is fond of things that are soft and tickle,' said the Bat. 'He is fond of warm things to hold in his arms when he goes to sleep. He is fond of being played with. He is fond of all those things.'

'Ah,' said the Cat, listening, 'then my time has come.'

Next night Cat walked through the Wet Wild Woods and hid very near the Cave till morning-time, and Man and Dog and Horse went hunting. The Woman was busy cooking that morning, and the Baby cried and interrupted. So she carried him outside the Cave and gave him a handful of **pebbles** to play with. But still the Baby cried.

Then the Cat put out his paddy paw and **patted** the Baby on the cheek, and it cooed; and the Cat rubbed against its fat knees and tickled it under its fat chin with his tail. And the Baby laughed; and the Woman heard him and smiled.

Then the Bat – the little upside-down bat – that hung in the mouth of the Cave said, 'O my Hostess and Wife of my Host and

Mother of my Host's Son, a Wild Thing from the Wild Woods is most beautifully playing with your Baby.'

'A **blessing** on that Wild Thing whoever he may be,' said the Woman, straightening her back, 'for I was a busy woman this morning and he has done me a service.'

That very minute and second, Best Beloved, the dried horse-skin Curtain that was stretched tail-down at the mouth of the Cave fell down – whoosh! – because it remembered the bargain she had made with the Cat, and when the Woman went to pick it up – **lo and behold**! – the Cat was sitting quite **comfy** inside the Cave.

'O my Enemy and Wife of my Enemy and Mother of my Enemy,' said the Cat, 'it is I: for you have spoken a word in my praise, and now I can sit within the Cave for always and always and always. But still I am the Cat who walks by himself, and all places are alike to me.'

The Woman was very angry, and shut her lips tight and took up her spinning-wheel[9] and began to spin. But the Baby cried because the Cat had gone away, and the Woman could not hush it, for it struggled and kicked and grew black in the face.

'O my Enemy and Wife of my Enemy and Mother of my Enemy,' said the Cat, 'take a strand of the wire that you are spinning and tie it to your spinning-whorl[10] and drag it along the floor, and I will show you a magic that shall make your Baby laugh as loudly as he is now crying.'

'I will do so,' said the Woman, 'because I am **at my wits' end**; but I will not thank you for it.'

She tied the thread to the little clay spindle whorl and drew it across the floor, and the Cat ran after it and patted it with his paws and rolled **head over heels**, and tossed it backward over his shoulder and chased it between his hind-legs and pretended to lose it, and pounced down upon it again, till the Baby laughed as loudly as it had been crying, and scrambled after the Cat and

9 a piece of equipment used in the past for making thread from wool or cotton
10 a small wheel in a spinning wheel

frolicked all over the Cave till it grew tired and settled down to sleep with the Cat in its arms.

'Now,' said the Cat, 'I will sing the Baby a song that shall keep him asleep for an hour.' And he began to purr, loud and low, low and loud, till the Baby fell fast asleep. The Woman smiled as she looked down upon the two of them and said, 'That was wonderfully done. No question but you are very clever, O Cat.'

That very minute and second, Best Beloved, the smoke of the fire at the back of the Cave came down in clouds from the roof – puff! – because it remembered the bargain she had made with the Cat, and when it had cleared away – lo and behold! – the Cat was sitting quite comfy close to the fire.

'O my Enemy and Wife of my Enemy and Mother of My Enemy,' said the Cat, 'it is I, for you have spoken a second word in my praise, and now I can sit by the warm fire at the back of the Cave for always and always and always. But still I am the Cat who walks by himself, and all places are alike to me.'

Then the Woman was very very angry, and let down her hair and put more wood on the fire and brought out the broad blade-bone of the shoulder of mutton and began to make a Magic that should prevent her from saying a third word in praise of the Cat. It was not a Singing Magic, Best Beloved, it was a Still Magic; and by and by the Cave grew so still that a little wee-wee[11] mouse crept out of a corner and ran across the floor.

'O my Enemy and Wife of my Enemy and Mother of my Enemy,' said the Cat, 'is that little mouse part of your magic?'

'Ouh! Chee! No indeed!' said the Woman, and she dropped the blade-bone and jumped upon the **footstool** in front of the fire and braided up her hair very quick for fear that the mouse should run up it.

'Ah,' said the Cat, watching, 'then the mouse will do me no harm if I eat it?'

'No,' said the Woman, braiding up her hair, 'eat it quickly and I will ever be grateful to you.'

11 in Scottish, *wee* means small

Cat made one jump and caught the little mouse, and the Woman said, 'A hundred thanks. Even the First Friend is not quick enough to catch little mice as you have done. You must be very wise.'

That very moment and second, O Best Beloved, the Milk-pot that stood by the fire cracked in two pieces – ffft – because it remembered the bargain she had made with the Cat, and when the Woman jumped down from the footstool – lo and behold! – the Cat was lapping up the warm white milk that lay in one of the broken pieces.

'O my Enemy and Wife of my Enemy and Mother of my Enemy,' said the Cat, 'it is I; for you have spoken three words in my praise, and now I can drink the warm white milk three times a day for always and always and always. But still I am the Cat who walks by himself, and all places are alike to me.'

Then the Woman laughed and set the Cat a bowl of the warm white milk and said, 'O Cat, you are as clever as a man, but remember that your bargain was not made with the Man or the Dog, and I do not know what they will do when they come home.'

'What is that to me?' said the Cat. 'If I have my place in the Cave by the fire and my warm white milk three times a day I do not care what the Man or the Dog can do.'

That evening when the Man and the Dog came into the Cave, the Woman told them all the story of the bargain while the Cat sat by the fire and smiled. Then the Man said, 'Yes, but he has not made a bargain with me or with all proper Men after me.' Then he took off his two leather boots and he took up his little stone axe (that makes three) and he fetched a piece of wood and a **hatchet** (that is five altogether), and he set them out in a row and he said, 'Now we will make our bargain. If you do not catch mice when you are in the Cave for always and always and always, I will throw these five things at you whenever I see you, and so shall all proper Men do after me.'

'Ah,' said the Woman, listening, 'this is a very clever Cat, but he is not so clever as my Man.'

The Cat counted the five things (and they looked very **knobby**) and he said, 'I will catch mice when I am in the Cave for always and always and always; but still I am the Cat who walks by himself, and all places are alike to me.'

'Not when I am near,' said the Man. 'If you had not said that last I would have put all these things away for always and always and always; but I am now going to throw my two boots and my little stone axe (that makes three) at you whenever I meet you. And so shall all proper Men do after me!'

Then the Dog said, 'Wait a minute. He has not made a bargain with me or with all proper Dogs after me.' And he showed his teeth and said, 'If you are not kind to the Baby while I am in the Cave for always and always and always, I will hunt you till I catch you, and when I catch you I will bite you. And so shall all proper Dogs do after me.'

'Ah,' said the Woman, listening, 'this is a very clever Cat, but he is not so clever as the Dog.'

Cat counted the Dog's teeth (and they looked very pointed) and he said, 'I will be kind to the Baby while I am in the Cave, as long as he does not pull my tail too hard, for always and always and always. But still I am the Cat that walks by himself, and all places are alike to me.'

'Not when I am near,' said the Dog. 'If you had not said that last I would have shut my mouth for always and always and always; but now I am going to hunt you up a tree whenever I meet you. And so shall all proper Dogs do after me.'

Then the Man threw his two boots and his little stone axe (that makes three) at the Cat, and the Cat ran out of the Cave and the Dog chased him up a tree; and from that day to this, Best Beloved, three proper Men out of five will always throw things at a Cat whenever they meet him, and all proper Dogs will chase him up a tree. But the Cat keeps his side of the bargain too. He will kill mice and he will be kind to Babies when he is in the house, just as long as they do not pull his tail too hard. But when he has done that, and between times, and when the moon gets up and night comes, he is the Cat that walks by himself, and all places are alike to him. Then he goes out to the Wet Wild Woods or up the Wet Wild Trees or on the Wet Wild Roofs, waving his wild tail and walking by his wild lone.

PUSSY can sit by the fire and sing,
Pussy can climb a tree,
Or play with a silly old cork and string
To 'muse[12] herself, not me.
But I like Binkie my dog, because
He knows how to behave;
So, Binkie's the same as the First Friend was,
And I am the Man in the Cave.

Pussy will play man-Friday[13] till
It's time to wet her paw
And make her walk on the window-sill
(For the footprint Crusoe saw);
Then she fluffles her tail and **mews**,
And scratches and won't attend.
But Binkie will play whatever I choose,
And he is my true First Friend!

Pussy will rub my knees with her head
Pretending she loves me hard;
But the very minute I go to my bed
Pussy runs out in the yard,
And there she stays till the morning-light;
So I know it is only pretend;
But Binkie, he snores at my feet all night,
And he is my Firstest Friend!

12 amuse
13 a man who helps someone with their work. Man Friday was Robinson Crusoe's helper in the novel by Daniel Defoe.

Post-reading activities

Understanding the story

Use these questions to help you check that you have understood the story.

1   How is the cat different from the other animals?
2   What do you understand by the phrase: 'All places are alike to him'?
3   How does the woman civilize the man?
4   Why is the man happy when he goes to sleep in front of the fire?
5   What does the 'singing magic' do?
6   Why are the animals interested in the light in the cave?
7   Why does the dog decide to investigate?
8   What makes the woman laugh when the dog arrives?
9   What bargain does the woman make with the dog?
10 Why does she cut the grass from the water-meadow?
11 Why does the horse go to the cave?
12 What bargain does the woman make with the horse?
13 Why does the cat decide to speak to the woman?
14 The woman explains to the cat that they have no need of any more animals. Is she right? Why? Why not?
15 What bargain does she make with the cat? Why?
16 What happens when the woman praises the cat each time?
17 What different techniques does the cat use for making the baby calm and happy?
18 What does the woman do to stop herself from praising the cat a third time? Why doesn't it work?
19 How does the woman's attitude to the cat change after she praises him the third time?
20 In what way is the bargain between the man and the cat different from all the previous bargains?
21 Why do the man and dog cancel the bargain?
22 What is the connection between the story and the poem?

Language study

Grammar

Uses of *so*

The word *so* has several uses in everyday English. Some of them are illustrated in these examples from the story.

a) *Then the Man went to sleep in front of the fire **ever so happy**.*
b) *'What is this that smells **so good** in the Wild Woods?'*
c) *Why should I not go too and see and look and come away at my own liking.' **So** he slipped after Wild Dog.*
d) *'This is a very wise Woman, but she is **not so wise as** I am.'*
e) *By and by the Cave grew **so still that** a little wee-wee mouse crept out of a corner and ran across the floor.*
f) *'I will throw these five things at you whenever I see you, and **so will** all proper Men do after me.'*
g) *The **Just So** Stories for Little Children*

1 **Look at these uses of *so* (1–5) and fill the gaps with words and phrases from the examples (a-g).**

1 *So* as a modifier
   So + adjective
   When *so* is followed by an adjective, it emphasizes a quality or feeling, e.g. *'What is this that smells* (1)......................... *in the Wild Woods?'*.
   We can use the adverb (2)......................... to emphasize this quality more, e.g. '(3)......................... *happy*'.

   So much/many
   With a noun, use *so much* or *so many* to emphasize the amount or number of something, e.g. *so many people*. With a verb, use *so much* after the verb for emphasis, e.g. *He always eats so much!*

   Explaining cause and effect
   We may want to explain the result of something. The result is introduced with the word 'that', e.g. '(4)......................... *a little wee-wee mouse crept out of a corner and ran across the floor*'.

   So + verbs of emotion
   When *so* is used before verbs of emotion, such as *love*, *appreciate* and *enjoy*, it emphasizes the strength of the emotion, e.g. *She **so enjoys** coming to your house to play.*

2   (*not*) *so* + adjective + *as*
    When *so* is used with an adjective followed by *as*, it is used to
    compare two things. For example, when the cat compares himself to
    the woman, he says, '... *she is* (5) .... *I am*'.

    As + adjective + *as* is a more common variation, e.g. *He is not as tall*
    as his brother.

3   *So* as a conjunction
    So can be used to link ideas that are related in terms of cause and
    result. It is used for saying that something happens, or someone
    does something, because of what has just been mentioned, e.g. '*Why*
    should I not go too and see and look and come away at my own liking.'
    (6) .... *after Wild Dog.*

    The following extract shows that we can use *so that* when the result
    is intended:

    > *The Woman cut great green armfuls of fresh grass from the water-*
    > *meadows, and dried it before the fire, so that it smelt like new-mown*
    > *hay.*

    The woman dried the grass because she wanted it to smell like fresh
    hay. *So that* is often shortened to *so* in everyday conversation.

4   Avoiding repetition
    So is used to avoid repetition of verbs, e.g. '*I will throw...*, *and* (7)
    .... *all proper Men do after me.*' What the man says about
    himself is also true about all men in the future. Here, *so* goes before
    the auxiliary verb and the subject, which are inverted: *so* + auxiliary
    verb + subject.

    It is also possible to put *so* after the verb, e.g. '*... and all proper Men*
    *will do **so** after me*'.

5   Expressions with *so*
    So has other meanings when used in fixed expressions with other
    words. A good dictionary will help you clarify their meaning and
    use.

    A less common use of *so* is illustrated in the title of the collection of
    short stories in which *The Cat that Walked by Himself* was published,
    e.g. '(8) *The* .... *for Little Chidren*'

    You can read an explanation of this expression in the section about
    origin stories in the Background information on page 13.

2 Use **THREE** words to complete the second sentence with the same meaning as the first. One of the words must be *so*.

1 Because he was born in France, he also has a French passport.
   He was born in France, ... has a French passport.
2 The children were far too excited to sleep.
   The children couldn't sleep because they .... excited.
3 Everything's changed to such an extent that I can scarcely recognize the place.
   Everything's changed .... I can scarcely recognize the place.
4 My parents send their love. Rachel does, too.
   My parents send their love, ... Rachel.
5 She loved watching the children play so much.
   .... watching the children play.
6 The road surface melted because it got very hot.
   The road surface became .... it melted.
7 You can learn to drive a car if I can.
   If I can learn how to drive a car, ...
8 It was not possible to see inside as the window was covered.
   The window was covered .... was not possible to see inside.

Linkers

The connections between sentences and ideas in *The Cat that Walked by Himself* are usually very simple. Notice the linking words and techniques in the third paragraph:

> *That night, Best Beloved, they ate wild sheep roasted on the hot stones, **and** flavoured with wild garlic **and** wild pepper; **and** wild duck stuffed with wild rice **and** wild fenugreek **and** wild coriander; **and** marrow-bones of wild oxen; **and** wild cherries, **and** wild grenadillas. **Then** the Man went to sleep in front of the fire ever so happy; **but** the Woman sat up, combing her hair. She took the bone of the shoulder of mutton – the big fat blade-bone – **and** she looked at the wonderful marks on it, **and** she threw more wood on the fire, **and** she made a Magic. She made the First Singing Magic in the world.*

3 Look at the linkers in the paragraph. Which linker:

a) contrasts two ideas, or identifies differences between them?
b) adds similar things or ideas to one another?
c) indicates the order in time between two actions?

The same linker may have more than one function. For example, when used after a negative *but* can introduce something that is true, e.g. *'His name is **not** Wild Dog any more, **but** the First Friend, because he will be our friend for always and always and always.'*

You could also say the same thing using *instead*, e.g. *His Friend **instead** of Wild Dog.*

Different linkers may share the same function.

4 Look at the linkers in bold in the extracts (1–6). Which function (a–d) do they share?

1 *'A blessing on that Wild Thing ...,'* said the Woman ..., *'**for** I was a busy woman this morning and he has done me a service.'*
2 *'Help my Man to hunt through the day and guard this Cave at night, **and** I will give you as many roast bones as you need.'*
3 *'... You have spoken a word in my praise, and **now** I can sit within the Cave ...'*
4 *'Nenni!'* said the Cat. *'... I will not come.'* *'**Then** we can never be friends again,'* said Wild Dog.
5 *He will kill mice and he will be kind to Babies when he is in the house, **just as long as** they do not pull his tail too hard.*
6 *Next day, holding her wild head high **that** her wild horns should not catch in the wild trees, Wild Cow came up to the Cave.*

a) contrast
b) comparison
c) cause and effect
d) addition

5 Replace each of the words or phrases in bold in exercise 4 with one of the alternatives in the box.

so that	only if	in which case
because	as a consequence	(if you...) then

6 Rewrite the sentences replacing *and, because,* or *but* with <u>one</u> of the linkers given in brackets. You may need to reorganize the sentence and change the punctuation.

1 She watched the match *and* immediately left for the hotel. (*that / then / though*)
2 She began to grow nervous, *because* he had promised to meet her at dawn. (*only if / for / then*)

3 I got some beefburgers for the barbecue *and* six kebabs. (**as well as** / **instead of** / **as long as**)
4 I can leave work early *because* Mr Griffiths has given me permission. (**then** / **in which case** / **now that**)
5 He's got a good job now *but* he still complains. (**although** / **instead** / **that**)
6 I never take a bath in the summer *but* a nice cold shower. (**as long as** / **for** / **instead of**)
7 He read the book quickly *because* he had to give it back the following day. (**then** / **so** / **that**)
8 Do the housework I asked you to do *and* I'll buy you an ice cream. (**if** / **however** / **that**)

Literary analysis

Plot

1 Write a one-sentence summary of the plot.
2 How many times does the cat follow the other animals to the cave? How many times does the woman speak words of praise about the cat? Can you think of other stories which repeat elements of the plot this many times?
3 Why does the cat think the other animals are foolish?
4 What is the bargain that the cat makes with the woman? How is it different from those of the dog, horse and cow?
5 Do you think the woman really performed magic, or is this just another way of saying that the delicious smells of the food and the hay attracted the animals to her? Justify your answer.
6 Does the cat show any magic of his own? What?
7 What could the cat have done to avoid being attacked by the man and chased by the dog?
8 How does the story describe the different roles of women and men?
9 How does the poem relate to the story?
10 Which of the words below would you use to describe the story? Why?

amusing	serious
childish	silly
clever	truthful
fantastical	your own description

11 Although the story was written in the 20th century, it is similar in many ways to a traditional folk tale or fairy tale. What are some of the story elements that make it seem much older than it really is?

Animals in the story

12 Make a list of all the animals mentioned in the story. Have any of the animals in the story not been domesticated?
13 What do the different domesticated animals do for the humans in the story?

Personification

Personification is the practice of showing human characteristics in things that are not human. In literature, things which are commonly personified include natural events like the weather, objects and animals. Children's literature is full of animals that talk, wear clothes, show human emotions and live human-like lives.

14 What human characteristics do the animals in the story have?
15 Certain animals are given stereotypical human qualities in stories about them. The fox, for example, is supposed to be cunning; that is, it uses its intelligence to get what it wants, especially by tricking or cheating people. What human qualities are given to the dog and cat?
16 What is the relationship between the animals like at the beginning of the story? Does it change at all through the story?

Character

17 Who is the main human character? Why is this character important in the story?
18 What motivates the woman?
19 How are the man and woman different in character?
20 In what sense is the man the first animal to be domesticated?
21 If there was a bargain between the woman and the man, what would it be?
22 Do the man and woman conform to any stereotypes of their sex?
23 Are there any baddies in the story? Who might be thought of as bad and why?
24 Do you sympathise with the cat at all?

Narration

25 At the beginning of the story, why does the storyteller ask the reader to 'listen' rather than to read?

26 How does the storyteller address the listener? What effect does this have on you?

27 What impression do you have of the storyteller?

28 Imagine that you were the storyteller reading the tale to a child. Read a section out loud. What kind of tone did you use? In what way was your voice different from when you are taking part in a conversation?

Style

29 Read the first sentence of the story again. Identify the verbs which ask the listener to pay attention and the verbs which express that it is a true story. What is the effect of saying the same thing more than once in this way?

30 Does this introduction to the story suggest that the story will be serious? What style of literature is it copying? How does this style complement the story?

31 Read the first paragraph. How many times is the word *wild* repeated? What is the effect of this in setting the scene for the story?

32 What do you notice about the following expressions? What effect does this have?

He will be our friend for always and always and always.

Cat went far and far away.

That very minute and second, ... the dried horse-skin Curtain ... fell down.

He began to purr, loud and low, low and loud.

33 In the story, capital letters are used at the beginning of many nouns that in normal English would not be capitalised. Find five words that are capitalized in this way. Thinking about the normal functions of capital letters, what effect does this have?

34 What effect does the simplified form of linking ideas and clauses with *and* and *but* have on a paragraph and on the story as a whole?

35 Read the final sentence of the story again. What does it have in common with the first paragraph of the story? What is the effect of this? Why isn't it in the same tense as the first paragraph?

Then he goes out to the Wet Wild Woods or up the Wet Wild Trees or on the Wet Wild Roofs, waving his wild tail and walking by his wild lone.

Guidance to the above literary terms, answer keys to all the exercises and activities, plus a wealth of other reading-practice material, can be found at: www.macmillanenglish.com/readers.

The Princess and the Puma
by O Henry

About the author

William Sydney Porter was the real name of the American short-story writer O Henry. Henry was very famous and popular in his day, and he is often referred to as the father of the modern short story. His stories have been translated into dozens of languages and are included in numerous anthologies. Even today, he remains one of the best-known and best-loved American short-story writers.

O Henry was born in 1862 in Greensboro, North Carolina. His mother died of tuberculosis when he was three, so he was raised by his grandmother and his aunt. As a child, he loved reading. One of his favourite books was the classic short-story collection, *One Thousand and One Nights*.

At the age of 15 he left school and started working with his uncle in his drugstore, where he trained to be a pharmacist. Then, when he was 20, he left Greensboro and moved to Texas. For two years he worked on a sheep ranch, looking after the sheep, as a general farm hand and cook. Still living in Texas, he moved to the city of Austin where he held several jobs over the next few years as a pharmacist, a journalist and a bank clerk at the Austin National Bank. He also met and married Athol Estes there. Two years later they had a daughter, Margaret.

During his time at the bank in Austin, O Henry started publishing a humorous magazine called *The Rolling Stone*, which included short stories and amusing writings by Henry himself. When he lost his job at the bank, he began working on *The Rolling Stone* full time. But although the magazine was popular and sold well, it didn't make enough money to support his family. Henry eventually closed down the magazine and moved to Houston where he started writing for the *Houston Post*.

A few years after he moved to Houston, Henry was arrested and accused of stealing money from the Austin National Bank where he had previously worked. The day before his trial he escaped, first to New Orleans and then to Honduras. He planned to wait there for his wife and daughter to join him and start a new life. However, Athol was too ill with tuberculosis to travel. When Henry heard that his wife was dying, he went back to Texas to be with her and he eventually went on trial for embezzlement. He was found guilty.

He spent three years of his five-year sentence in a prison in Ohio, where he first started writing stories under the name of O Henry. He left prison in 1901; shortly after this, he moved to New York, where he lived for the next eight years until his death in 1910. During that period he wrote over 300 short stories.

Henry's first collection, *Cabbages And Kings*, appeared in 1904. The second, *The Four Million*, was published two years later and included one of his best-known stories, *The Gift of the Magi*, which you can read in the Macmillan Literature collection *American Stories*. O Henry wrote more than 600 short stories. He published ten collections during his lifetime and three more were published after his death.

His stories mainly deal with ordinary people and their lives. Many are based in New York but he also wrote about Texas and Honduras, among other places. Many of his stories have a surprise ending. His stories tend to be humorous and optimistic, which may be one reason that they remain popular to this day.

About the story

The Princess and the Puma was first published in 1907. It was one of a collection of short stories by O Henry called *Heart of the West*, about country life in the western United States.

Background information

The ranch

A ranch is any very large farm in North America where cows, horses, or sheep are kept. When farmers came to the south and west of North America from Britain, Ireland, Spain and other countries in Europe, they were faced with very different farming conditions from those that they were used to. This was because in Europe higher rainfall provided good grass to feed the animals so smaller farms were possible. Also, small farms are necessary in developed countries with high populations where there is not much space. But with the drier climate, large open prairies and the grasslands of the central United States, a better way to raise cattle (cows), horses or sheep was to allow them to travel longer distances to look for food.

The one place in Europe that did look very like these dry grasslands was southern Spain. There, *vaqueros*, or cowboys, had learnt to use horses to control herds of cattle over large distances. Their techniques were adopted in Mexico and the United States and 'cowboy' culture was born.

Ranches need good organisation to work well, so the people who work on a ranch are organized into teams, or outfits, which are managed by a foreman. Each outfit will include people who stay with the sheep or cattle and look after them, called herders, as well as specialists, called wranglers, who know best how to handle horses and control the animals.

The largest ranches of this type are now found in Australia. They are not called ranches there, but cattle or sheep stations. The largest covers 24,000 km^2, four times larger than the biggest American ranch.

Spanish in the English language

A number of Spanish words have entered the English language through the ranch culture of the south-western United States. Many people who lived and worked on farms there were Spanish speaking, and the Spanish influence was very strong. *The Princess and the Puma* is set in southern Texas, on the Mexican border, in a part of the United States that belonged to Mexico before 1836, and so the story naturally includes various Spanish words. The mother of one of the main characters was a Mexican from Laredo, a town on the US border, and her daughter's name, Josefa O'Donnell, shows this cultural mix of Irish American and Spanish. Her first name is Spanish and her surname is Irish.

Spanish words in the story which have entered into English include *arroyo* and *coyote*. Both are words with special meanings with local significance. An *arroyo* is a narrow valley in a North or South American desert that is usually dry but carries water during a rain storm. A *coyote* is a wild dog that lives in North America.

The puma

The puma in the title of the story relates to a species of cat that lives in North and South America. It is also known as the cougar — or mountain lion — and in the story is referred to as the Mexican lion. In fact, the species *Puma concolor* holds the Guinness World Record for the animal with the most names, including 40 in English.

Although sometimes called a lion, it is not related to the African lion and is not even classified as one of the big cats, being more closely related to the domestic cat. It is smaller than a lion and cannot make the roaring sound made by big cats like lions and tigers, though it does sometimes make a noise like a scream.

Even so, it is still about the size of an adult human, and has been known to kill people, though not very often. It usually kills deer and smaller animals by hiding and waiting before leaping on top of them by surprise.

Summary

It may help you to know something about what happens in the story before you read it. Don't worry, this summary does not tell you how the story ends!

Josefa O'Donnell is the daughter of Ben O'Donnell, the cattle farmer whose land provides the setting for the story. He owns Espinosa Ranch — the biggest in the area — and has the most cows, and because of this, he is known as the 'Cattle King'. Josefa is beautiful like her mother, but she is also brave and confident like her father, and has learnt many skills from him, such as how to use a gun and ride a horse. This combination makes her very popular with the men who work on the ranch, all of whom are happy to work for her. If Ben O'Donnell is the king in their world, Josefa is their princess.

One man on the ranch, Ripley Givens, is particularly attracted to Josefa and wants to marry her. He is one of the Espinosa foremen, who, at the beginning of the story, is returning to his camp from a nearby ranch. Some young cows are lost so he is looking for them. Now it is late, and he decides not to continue on his journey back home because he is tired. Instead, he sets up camp ready to spend the night by a river crossing. He ties up his horse near some grass and sits down to smoke a cigarette. That is when he and his horse hear a noise. They both recognize it. It is the cry of a puma and it frightens the horse. Ripley is not scared, but he prepares his gun in case he needs it.

Then he notices an old empty metal can that another traveller has left by the camp. He realizes he can use it to make himself a cup of coffee. So he makes a fire and walks to the water hole in the river bed. As he approaches the dry river he sees Josefa O'Donnell and her horse, who have been drinking water there. But they are not alone. Hiding behind a bush close to Josefa, the puma is crouching down, ready to leap towards her. What can Ripley do? Unfortunately he has left his gun back near his horse, away from the river. There is only one thing to do. He gives a loud shout and runs straight between the puma and the princess.

What happens next may determine his future with Josefa. Will he become a hero? Will he just make himself look stupid? Or is the real story more complicated than that?

Pre-reading activities

Key vocabulary

This section will help you familiarize yourself with some of the more specific vocabulary used in the story. You may want to use it to help you before you start reading, or as a revision exercise after you have finished the story.

Words associated with horses, cattle and cowboys

The story is set on a cattle ranch; the main characters live and work with cows and horses.

1 **Match the words in bold in the sentences (1–11) below with their definitions (a–k).**

1 He looked like a real little cowboy, from the hat all the way down to the **spurs**.

2 His horse was tired after the long journey, so he took off the **saddle** and let it rest.

3 Paul could be identified from a distance because of his distinctive **gait**, long before his face was discernable.

4 Ripley hit the animal on its **hind quarters** to set it running towards the waiting cowboys.

5 **Steers** are nearly always raised for their meat, having little value for the future of the herd.

6 The herd was young, mostly just **yearlings** and two-year-olds.

7 The horse took off at great speed across the farmyard. Harvey gripped the **reins** in terror.

8 These old cows are worth more at market **on the hoof** because they may still be able to produce calves.

9 They set off at a **gallop** to tell the rancher of the forest fire.

10 Knowing that lions had been seen in the area, he kept his **pistol** loaded and in his belt at all times.

11 He took no chances; as well as his hunting rifle he kept a **six-shooter** by the bed.

a) a leather seat that you put on a horse's back when you ride it

b) a long piece of leather fastened around a horse's head that the rider uses to control the horse

c) a metal object on a rider's boot that is pressed into a horse's side to make it go faster

d) a small gun that you hold in one hand

e) cows or horses that are between one and two years old

f) young male cows that have had their sex organs removed

g) still alive, not killed

h) a gun that holds six bullets

i) the back parts of an animal's body, including its back legs

j) the fastest speed of a horse

k) the way that a person or animal walks

Noises

2 Read the definitions of different sounds. What animal or animals might make each of the sounds: a horse, a puma, a human or other animals? Imagine what it would sound like.

contralto the lowest female singing voice

grunt a short low sound made by a person or an animal

rucus a fight, or a noisy argument

snort a sudden loud noise that you make through your nose, because you are angry or laughing for example

splash the sound of liquid hitting something, or the sound of something falling into a liquid

wail a shout, or cry with a long high sound to show that you are in pain or are very sad

yelp a short loud high noise that you make when you are excited, angry, or in pain

Verbs of movement

3 Read the words and definitions below then choose the correct word to complete the sentences (1–11).

drag pull something with difficulty

gouge push your fingers deep into someone (often into their eyes) to hurt them, normally in a fight

grope try to find something, or get to a place by feeling the way with your hands

jar push something firmly and suddenly against something else, usually accidentally

linger stay somewhere longer than is necessary because it is enjoyable

mingle mix two or more things together without losing their individual characters

plump drop, sink, or come in contact with something suddenly or heavily **rumple** make something untidy, or not smooth

skip move forwards by jumping first on one foot and then the other

stoop bend the top half of your body downwards

waver if a person wavers, they are not certain about what to say or do

1 Alfred has not **mingled / wavered** from his decision to move to France.
2 He **gouged / dragged** the boy slowly out from under the tree.
3 He located his mobile at the bottom of his bag after **groping / lingering** for it for several seconds.
4 He **rumpled / groped** the bed to make it look as if he had slept in it.
5 I must have **jarred / dragged** my shoulder playing basketball.
6 Julie **rumpled / skipped** along the pavement, holding her teddy bear.
7 Polly felt hope **mingled / lingered** with fear.
8 Sally **stooped / plumped** the box on the table and left.
9 She let her eyes **linger / mingle** on him a little longer.
10 She **jarred / stooped** and kissed the children.
11 He fought like a wild animal, **gouging / plumping** his fingers into his opponent's face.

Main themes

Before you read the story, you may want to think about some of its main themes. The questions will help you think about the story as you are reading it for the first time. There is more discussion of the main themes in the *Literary analysis* section after the story.

Feminine and masculine roles

Ideas of femininity and masculinity are central to the story, which tells of the meeting of a woman and a man in unusual circumstances in the middle of the countryside, far from the comforts of home.

4 While you are reading the story, consider the following questions:

a) Traditionally, what role would a man be expected to take in such situations? How would a woman be expected to react?
b) In what ways is the man masculine? In what ways is the woman feminine?
c) Do either of them adopt roles which are not typical of their sex?

Saving face

If you are trying to save face, you want to avoid seeming stupid or feeling embarrassed.

5 As you read the story, ask yourself:

a) Who wants to save face?
b) Why is it important to them not to be embarrassed?
c) What do they do to save face?

Making a good impression

Ripley Givens has a romantic interest in Josefa O' Donnell. When they meet, he tries to impress her. She is also keen to make a good impression on him.

6 As you read the story, think about the following questions:

a) How do they impress each other?
b) Is it always a good idea to try to impress?
c) Are their reasons for impressing the other person the same?

The Princess and the Puma

by O Henry

There had to be a king and queen, of course. The king was a terrible old man who wore six-shooters and spurs, and shouted in such a tremendous voice that the rattlers[1] on the prairie would run into their holes under the prickly pear. Before there was a royal family they called the man 'Whispering Ben.' When he came to own 50,000 acres[2] of land and more cattle than he could count, they called him O'Donnell 'the Cattle King.'

The queen had been a Mexican girl from Laredo. She made a good, mild, Colorado-claro[3] wife, and even succeeded in teaching Ben to modify his voice sufficiently while in the house to keep the dishes from being broken. When Ben got to be king she would sit on the gallery of Espinosa Ranch and **weave** rush mats. When wealth became so irresistible and **oppressive** that upholstered chairs and a centre table were brought down from San Antone in the wagons, she bowed her smooth, dark head, and shared the fate of the Danae[4].

To avoid *lèse-majesté*[5] you have been presented first to the king and queen. They do not enter the story, which might be called 'The Chronicle of the Princess, the Happy Thought, and the Lion that **Bungled** his Job.'

Josefa O'Donnell was the surviving daughter, the princess. From her mother she inherited warmth of nature and a dusky[6], semi-tropic beauty. From Ben O'Donnell the royal she acquired a store of **intrepidity**, common sense, and the faculty of ruling.

1 *informal*: a rattlesnake, a snake that makes a noise with its tail that sounds like a rattle
2 a unit for measuring land area. 1 acre = 4046 m^2
3 light brown in colour
4 in Greek mythology, the daughter of a king who locked her away from other people
5 *French*: the act of saying or doing something that will offend a king or ruler
6 with dark skin. This word is now considered offensive.

The combination was one worth going miles to see. Josefa while riding her pony at a gallop could put five out of six bullets through a tomato-can swinging at the end of a string. She could play for hours with a white kitten she owned, dressing it in all manner of absurd clothes. **Scorning** a pencil, she could tell you out of her head what 1,545 two-year-olds would bring on the hoof, at $8.50 per head. Roughly speaking, the Espinosa Ranch is forty miles long and thirty broad – but mostly **leased** land. Josefa, on her pony, had **prospected** over every mile of it. Every cow-puncher[7] on the range knew her by sight and was a loyal vassal[8]. Ripley Givens, foreman of one of the Espinosa outfits, saw her one day, and made up his mind to form a royal matrimonial[9] alliance. **Presumptuous**? No. In those days in the Nueces country a man was a man. And, after all, the title of cattle king does not presuppose blood royalty. Often it only signifies that its owner wears the crown **in token of** his magnificent qualities in the art of cattle stealing.

One day Ripley Givens rode over to the Double Elm Ranch to inquire about a bunch of **strayed** yearlings. He was late in setting out on his return trip, and it was sundown when he struck the White Horse Crossing of the Nueces. From there to his own camp it was sixteen miles. To the Espinosa ranch it was twelve. Givens was tired. He decided to pass the night at the Crossing.

There was a fine water hole in the river-bed. The banks were thickly covered with great trees, undergrown with brush[10]. Back from the water hole fifty yards[11] was a stretch of curly mesquite grass – supper for his horse and bed for himself. Givens staked his horse, and spread out his saddle blankets to dry. He sat down with his back against a tree and rolled a cigarette. From somewhere in the dense **timber** along the river came a sudden, rageful, **shivering** wail. The pony danced at the end of his rope and blew

---

7 *old-fashioned, informal:* cowboy
8 *literary:* someone during the Middle Ages who was loyal to a king who gave them a home and protection
9 *formal:* relating to marriage
10 *US English:* an area of land with small trees and bushes growing on it
11 1 yard = 91 cm. There are three feet in one yard.

a whistling snort of comprehending fear. Givens puffed at his cigarette, but he reached leisurely for his pistol-belt, which lay on the grass, and twirled the cylinder of his weapon tentatively. A great gar[12] plunged with a loud splash into the water hole. A little brown rabbit skipped around a bunch of catclaw[13] and sat twitching his whiskers and looking humorously at Givens. The pony went on eating grass.

It is well[14] to be reasonably watchful when a Mexican lion sings soprano along the arroyos at sundown. The **burden** of his song may be that young calves and fat lambs are **scarce**, and that he has a carnivorous desire for your acquaintance[15].

In the grass lay an empty fruit can, cast there by some former **sojourner**. Givens caught sight of it with a grunt of satisfaction. In his coat pocket tied behind his saddle was a handful or two of ground coffee. Black coffee and cigarettes! What ranchero could desire more?

In two minutes he had a little fire going clearly. He started, with his can, for the water hole. When within fifteen yards of its edge he saw, between the bushes, a side-saddled[16] pony with down-dropped reins cropping grass a little distance to his left. Just rising from her hands and knees on the brink of the water hole was Josefa O'Donnell. She had been drinking water, and she brushed the sand from the palms of her hands. Ten yards away, to her right, half concealed by a **clump** of sacuista[17], Givens saw the crouching form of the Mexican lion. His **amber** eyeballs **glared** hungrily; six feet from them was the tip of the tail stretched straight, like a pointer's[18]. His hind-quarters rocked with the motion of the cat tribe preliminary to leaping.

Givens did what he could. His six-shooter was thirty-five yards away lying on the grass. He gave a loud yell, and dashed between the lion and the princess.

12 a freshwater fish from North America
13 a tree native to the southern United States and Mexico
14 *old-fashioned*: it is advisable, a good idea
15 *formal*: another way of saying that he wants to meet you so that he can eat you
16 a special saddle designed so that a woman can ride in a long skirt
17 a type of grass
18 a dog used in hunting that points its nose at birds and small animals

The 'rucus', as Givens called it afterward, was brief and somewhat confused. When he arrived on the line of attack he saw a dim **streak** in the air, and heard a couple of faint cracks. Then a hundred pounds of Mexican lion plumped down upon his head and flattened him, with a heavy jar, to the ground. He remembered calling out: 'Let up, now—no fair gouging!' and then he crawled from under the lion like a worm, with his mouth full of grass and dirt, and a big lump on the back of his head where it had struck the root of a water-elm. The lion lay motionless. Givens, feeling **aggrieved**, and suspicious of fouls, shook his fist at the lion, and shouted: 'I'll rastle you again for twenty—'[19] and then he got back to himself.

Josefa was standing in her tracks, quietly reloading her silver-mounted .38. It had not been a difficult shot. The lion's head made an easier mark than a tomato-can swinging at the end of a string. There was a **provoking, teasing,** maddening smile upon her mouth and in her dark eyes. The **would-be-**rescuing knight felt the fire of his **fiasco** burn down to his soul. Here had been his chance, the chance that he had dreamed of; and Momus[20], and not Cupid, had presided over it. The satyrs in the wood were, no doubt, holding their sides in hilarious, silent laughter. There had been something like vaudeville[21] – say Signor Givens and his funny knockabout act with the stuffed lion.

'Is that you, Mr Givens?' said Josefa, in her deliberate, **saccharine** contralto. 'You nearly spoilt my shot when you yelled. Did you hurt your head when you fell?'

'Oh, no,' said Givens, quietly; 'that didn't hurt.' He stooped ignominiously[22] and dragged his best Stetson hat from under the beast. It was crushed and **wrinkled** to a fine comedy effect. Then

19 I'll wrestle (fight) you again for twenty dollars.
20 in Greek mythology, Momus is a god who represents criticism and who laughs at people's stupidity. Cupid is a god of love. Satyrs are mythological creatures who live in the forest.
21 a type of popular entertainment of the late 19th and early 20th centuries. 'Signor Givens' is suggested as his stage name for a silly act involving him and a toy lion.
22 in a way that shows embarrassment or humiliation, especially because you seem or feel very unsuccessful or unimportant

he knelt down and softly stroked the fierce, open-jawed head of the dead lion.

'Poor old Bill!' he exclaimed mournfully.

'What's that?' asked Josefa, sharply.

'Of course you didn't know, Miss Josefa,' said Givens, with an **air** of one allowing magnanimity[23] to triumph over **grief**. 'Nobody can blame you. I tried to save him, but I couldn't let you know in time.'

'Save who?'

'Why, Bill. I've been looking for him all day. You see, he's been our camp pet for two years. Poor old fellow, he wouldn't have hurt a cottontail rabbit. It'll break the boys all up[24] when they hear about it. But you couldn't tell, of course, that Bill was just trying to play with you.'

Josefa's black eyes burned steadily upon him. Ripley Givens met the test successfully. He stood rumpling the yellow-brown curls on his head pensively. In his eye was regret, not unmingled with a gentle **reproach**. His smooth features were set to a pattern of **indisputable** sorrow. Josefa wavered.

'What was your pet doing here?' she asked, making a last stand. 'There's no camp near the White Horse Crossing.'

'The old **rascal** ran away from camp yesterday,' answered Givens readily. 'It's a wonder the coyotes didn't scare him to death. You see, Jim Webster, our horse wrangler, brought a little terrier pup into camp last week. The pup made life miserable for Bill—he used to chase him around and chew his hind legs for hours at a time. Every night when bedtime came Bill would sneak under one of the boy's blankets and sleep to keep the pup from finding him. I reckon he must have been worried pretty desperate or he wouldn't have run away. He was always afraid to get out of sight of camp.'

Josefa looked at the body of the fierce animal. Givens gently patted one of the formidable paws that could have killed a yearling calf with one blow. Slowly a red flush widened upon

23 *formal*: a willingness to forgive people, or to be kind and fair
24 *informal*: make the other men in the camp unhappy

the dark olive face of the girl. Was it the signal of shame of the true sportsman who has brought down ignoble quarry[25]? Her eyes grew softer, and the lowered lids drove away all their bright **mockery**.

'I'm very sorry,' she said humbly; 'but he looked so big, and jumped so high that–'

'Poor old Bill was hungry,' interrupted Givens, in quick defence of the deceased[26].' We always made him jump for his supper in camp. He would lie down and roll over for a piece of meat. When he saw you he thought he was going to get something to eat from you.'

Suddenly Josefa's eyes opened wide.

'I might have shot you!' she exclaimed. 'You ran right in between. You risked your life to save your pet! That was fine, Mr Givens. I like a man who is kind to animals.'

Yes; there was even admiration in her **gaze** now. After all, there was a hero rising out of the ruins of the **anti-climax**. The look on Givens's face would have secured him a high position in the S.P.C.A.[27]

'I always loved 'em,' said he; 'horses, dogs, Mexican lions, cows, alligators–'

'I hate alligators,' instantly demurred Josefa; 'crawly, muddy things!'

'Did I say alligators?' said Givens. 'I meant antelopes, of course.'

Josefa's conscience drove her to **make** further **amends**. She held out her hand **penitently**. There was a bright, unshed drop in each of her eyes.

'Please forgive me, Mr Givens, won't you? I'm only a girl, you know, and I was frightened at first. I'm very, very sorry I shot Bill. You don't know how ashamed I feel. I wouldn't have done it for anything.'

---

25 *formal*: an ignoble action should make you feel ashamed. The quarry is an animal that someone is trying to catch.
26 *formal*: the deceased means a dead person
27 the Society for the Prevention of Cruelty to Animals

Givens took the proffered hand. He held it for a time while he allowed the generosity of his nature to overcome his grief at the loss of Bill. At last it was clear that he had forgiven her.

'Please don't speak of it any more, Miss Josefa. 'Twas enough to frighten any young lady the way Bill looked. I'll explain it all right to the boys.'

'Are you really sure you don't hate me?' Josefa came closer to him impulsively. Her eyes were sweet – oh, sweet and pleading with gracious penitence. 'I would hate anyone who would kill my kitten. And how daring and kind of you to risk being shot when you tried to save him! How very few men would have done that!' Victory wrested[28] from defeat! Vaudeville turned into drama! Bravo, Ripley Givens!

It was now twilight. Of course Miss Josefa could not be allowed to ride on to the ranch-house alone. Givens resaddled his pony in spite of that animal's reproachful glances, and rode with her. Side by side they galloped across the smooth grass, the princess and the man who was kind to animals. The prairie odours of fruitful[29] earth and delicate bloom[30] were thick and sweet around them. Coyotes yelping over there on the hill! No fear. And yet –

Josefa rode closer. A little hand seemed to grope. Givens found it with his own. The ponies kept an even gait. The hands lingered together, and the owner of one explained:

'I never was frightened before, but just think! How terrible it would be to meet a really wild lion! Poor Bill! I'm so glad you came with me!'

O'Donnell was sitting on the ranch gallery[31].

'Hello, Rip!' he shouted – 'that you?'

'He rode in with me,' said Josefa. 'I lost my way and was late.'

'Much obliged[32],' called the cattle king. 'Stop over, Rip, and ride to camp in the morning.'

28 *formal*: to pull something away from someone using force
29 *literary*: producing a lot of crops or fruit
30 *literary*: a lot of flowers or plants together
31 *US English*: a covered area along the outside of a house (*British English*: veranda)
32 *formal*: used for thanking someone politely

But Givens would not. He would push on to camp. There was a bunch of steers to start off on the trail at daybreak. He said good-night, and trotted away.

An hour later, when the lights were out, Josefa, in her night-robe, came to her door and called to the king in his own room across the brick-paved hallway:

'Say, pop, you know that old Mexican lion they call the 'Gotch-eared Devil' – the one that killed Gonzales, Mr Martin's sheep herder, and about fifty calves on the Salado range? Well, I settled his hash[33] this afternoon over at the White Horse Crossing. Put two balls in his head with my .38 while he was on the jump. I knew him by the slice gone from his left ear that old Gonzales cut off with his **machete**. You couldn't have made a better shot yourself, daddy.'

'Bully for you[34]!' thundered Whispering Ben from the darkness of the royal chamber.

---

33 *old-fashioned, US English*: stop someone permanently from causing any more trouble
34 *old-fashioned*: Well done! Used for praising someone in a way that shows you are impressed with what they have done.

Post-reading activities

Understanding the story

Use these questions to help you check that you have understood the story.

1 Why is Ben O'Donnell given the name 'Whispering Ben'? Why 'the Cattle King'?

2 How is Josefa like her father? How is she like her mother?

3 What indications are there that Josefa will be a successful rancher like her father?

4 Why it is not unreasonable that Ripley should hope to marry Josefa, according to the storyteller?

5 What options does Ripley have when he arrives at White Horse Crossing? Why does he choose to stay?

6 What attracts Ripley to that particular place?

7 What do Ripley and his horse hear? How does the horse react to the noise? How does Ripley react?

8 What distracts him from the danger of the puma?

9 In what order does he first notice a) Josefa O'Donnell, b) her pony, c) the puma?

10 How well does Givens remember the attack?

11 How does he feel immediately after the attack? How does Josefa feel?

12 Where was Givens hurt? Why does he say that it doesn't hurt?

13 Why does he tell her that the puma is a pet?

14 How does Givens try to convince Josefa that the story is true?

15 Why had 'Bill' run away, according to Givens?

16 What does Josefa say she admires about Givens?

17 Why does Givens change his mind about liking alligators?

18 What excuse does Josefa give for shooting the animal?

19 Why are we told that 'Of course Miss Josefa could not be allowed to ride on to the ranch-house alone'?

20 What excuse do the coyotes provide Josefa?

21 What does O'Donnell offer Ripley? What excuse does Ripley give for refusing the offer?

22 What does Josefa tell her father at bedtime? How does this change the story?

Language study

Grammar

Talking about the past – modal verbs and the perfect infinitive

After Josefa shoots the puma, she and Ripley start talking about what has happened. On hearing Ripley's story, that the puma was a pet, Josefa expresses sorrow for her actions. At the same time, Ripley adds detail to his story and discusses what happened to Bill before the shooting in order to make his story seem more real. Notice the use of modal verbs:

> 'You don't know how ashamed I feel. I **wouldn't** have done it for anything.'

> 'I reckon he **must** have been worried pretty desperate.'

Form

Modal verbs must be followed by an infinitive. To make an infinitive for the past we can use the perfect infinitive: *have* + past participle:

> 'How very few men **would have done** that!'

Negative forms are possible:

> 'You **couldn't have made** a better shot yourself, daddy.'

Use

Modal verbs can be used to express a variety of emotions and thought processes about the past. Here are some examples:

> 'I reckon he **must** have been worried pretty desperate or he **wouldn't** have run away.' (speculation)

> 'I **might** have shot you!' she exclaimed. (regret)

> Givens gently patted one of the formidable paws that **could** have killed a yearling calf with one blow. (ability)

Here are some more possible speculations about the puma:
a) 'Bill may have followed me to White Horse Crossing.'
b) 'He can't have seen me before he went to you for food.'

1 **Underline the modal verbs in sentences (a) and (b) above. Which of these modal verbs has the same meaning as *might have*? Which is a synonym of *couldn't have*?**

2 Match the modal verbs in the box to their meanings (1–3) below.
   Note: More than one answer for some of the meanings is possible.

can't have	could have	couldn't have
may have	might have	must have

1 I am sure that this is what happened. It seems the only logical
   possibility.
2 I am sure that this did not happen.
3 I think this is a possible or logical explanation, but not the only one.

3 Look at the following sentences. Which express regret? Which
   express ability (or lack of ability)? Which describe hypothetical
   situations that did not happen? More than one answer for some of
   the sentences is possible.

1 He could have killed us both if he wanted.
2 I don't think I would have been able to kill it on my own.
3 I shouldn't have shot that poor animal.
4 You couldn't have known, Miss Josefa.
5 You should have told me it was your pet.
6 I couldn't have let you know in time to stop you from shooting him.

4 Rewrite the underlined sections of the following sentences using a
   modal verb and the perfect infinitive.

1 It's certain that Josefa didn't see Ripley before she took the shot.
2 Josefa wondered why the animal jumped: 'I'm sure Bill was hungry,'
   Ripley explained.
3 Ripley had had to run at the lion because he had no weapon: 'If only
   I had brought my gun to the water hole.'
4 It's possible to imagine Josefa accidently shooting Ripley.
5 'There was nothing else for you to do except take the shot, Josefa.'
6 Ripley was tired. 'I wish I'd had that coffee back at White Horse
   Crossing,' he said.
7 We are together now because that puma attacked. Imagine if it
   hadn't.

Verb patterns

Form

Look at some examples of different verb patterns from the story. Notice how the verbs combine with other words in different structures, or patterns.

a) *She ... **succeeded in teaching** Ben to modify his voice ...*

b) *She ... succeeded in **teaching Ben to modify** his voice ...*

c) *Ripley Givens ... **made up his mind to form** a royal matrimonial alliance.*

d) *The pony **went on eating** grass.*

e) *We always **made him jump** for his supper in camp.*

f) *Bill would sneak under ... the blankets ... to **keep the pup from finding** him.*

g) *You **risked your life to save** your pet!*

5 Match each of the example sentences (a–g) to the different verb patterns(1–7) below.

Verb + infinitive

1 Many verbs can be followed by a verb in the infinitive. Often, the infinitive is preceded by *to*, i.e. verb + *to* + infinitive:

    e.g. ....
    Other verbs with this pattern include: *agree, decide, hope, seem, want, try.*

2 Some verbs take an object and a verb, i.e. verb + object + *to* + infinitive:

    e.g. ....
    Other verbs with this pattern include: *allow, ask, force, invite, tell.*

3 A few verbs take an object and an infinitive without *to*, i.e. verb + object + infinitive:

    e.g. ....
    Other verbs with this pattern include: *let, help.*

4 Verbs can come after whole verb phrases to explain the reason why that action was taken. This is called the *infinitive of purpose*, i.e. verb phrase + *to* + infinitive:

    e.g. ....

Verb + gerund

5 Some verbs are followed by a gerund, i.e. verb + gerund:

e.g. ....

Other verbs with this pattern include: *avoid, consider, keep, don't mind, risk.*

6 Often, though, the gerund must be preceded by a preposition, i.e. verb + preposition + gerund:

e.g. ....

Other verbs with this pattern include: *think (about), believe (in), worry (about).*

7 Some verbs need an object, which precedes the gerund, i.e. verb + object + preposition + gerund:

e.g. ....

Other verbs with this pattern include: *accuse (someone of), save (someone from), thank (someone for).*

6 Complete these extracts with the verb in brackets in the infinitive (with or without *to*) or the gerund.

1 *He decided* .... (pass) *the night at the Crossing.*

2 *Givens ... spread out his saddle blankets* .... (dry).

3 *'How daring and kind of you to risk* .... (be shot) *when you tried* .... (save) *him!'*

4 *A little hand seemed* .... (grope).

5 *'I couldn't let you* .... (know) *in time.'*

6 *'Bill was just trying* .... (play) *with you.'*

7 Choose the correct verb pattern in these sentences.

1 *Are you accusing me* **to lie / of lying / about lying**?

2 *Foreign tourists can help* **revitalizing / revitalize / for revitalizing** *our economy.*

3 *Have you thought* **about talking / to talk / in talking** *to someone about the problem?*

4 *He's being forced* **resign / about resigning / to resign** *because of the allegations.*

5 *I don't believe* **to get / getting / in getting** *married for the sake of it.*

6 *I keep forgetting* **to turn / turn / turning** *the lights off when I leave.*

7 *She only allows the children* **in watching / to watch / watch** *television at weekends.*

8 *She's considering* **buying / to buy / of buying** *a second car.*

9 *The dishwasher saves us* **from washing / to wash / in washing** *-up after every meal.*

10 *The school agreed **in sending** / **to send** / **sending** the students on the course.*
11 *They've invited me **eat** / **to eat** / **in eating** at their house tonight.*
12 *They've lowered the price of the house **encourage** / **encouraging** / **to encourage** more offers.*

Literary analysis

Plot

1 Ben O'Donnell is not a real king and his daughter isn't a princess, but the story refers to them as royalty and so makes a connection to the genre of fairy tales. How is the plot similar to other stories of this genre? How is it different?
2 The story teller suggests an alternative title: 'The Chronicle of the Princess, the Happy Thought, and the Lion that Bungled his Job'. What, in your opinion, is the 'happy thought'? In what way did the 'lion bungle his job'?
3 What would have been the consequence if Josefa had not shot the puma?
4 What would have been the consequence if Ripley had not been able to make up the story about the puma in time?
5 Why does Josefa choose to go along with Ripley's story?
6 Why did Ripley decide to continue home in the end even though he was tired and had decided to camp the night at the water hole at the beginning of the story?
7 What do you think will happen now?
8 How do you think the event with the puma will be recorded by the people on the ranch: as a heroic moment for Ripley, or for Josefa, or will it be kept secret? Justify your answer.
9 What does the story say about men and women?

Character

10 Do you think Ben O'Donnell is a good father? Support your answer with evidence from the story.
11 Describe Josefa's relationship with her father.
12 How much is Josefa a princess and how much is she a tomboy (a girl who behaves like a boy and prefers activities that people think are more suitable for boys)?

13   Does Josefa's character stay the same or do we see different aspects of her personality at different stages of the story? Explain your answer.

14   Think of the character of Ripley. To what extent is he a stereotype of a cowboy as portrayed by Hollywood?

15   In what ways is Ripley:
   a) optimistic?   b) resourceful?
   c) responsible?   d) romantic?

16   How quickly does Ripley think of a way of not seeming so foolish after the shooting? What does that tell you about him?

17   In your opinion, would Ripley and Josefa make a good couple?

Animals in the story

18   Make a list of the animals that feature in the story. What is the proportion of domesticated animals to wild ones? How does this reflect the setting of the story?

19   What does the appearance of the puma at the water hole represent for Josefa? And for Ripley?

20   What is the puma like? How does this contrast with Ripley's portrayal of 'Bill'?

21   To what extent is Ripley's horse a character? What emotions does it show?

Narration

22   Look at the first sentence of the story again: *There had to be a king and queen, of course*. The story teller does not start telling the story immediately; instead, he comments on the story before starting. What effect does this have on how you read the story?

23   Another example of a comment like this, where the story teller speaks directly to the reader, is in the third paragraph. Why does the story begin the way it has in the first two paragraphs, according to the story teller?

24   Find an instance of the reader's voice in the fourth paragraph, where it seems as if the story teller is responding directly to what the reader has said. Why does he do this?

25 Read the scene by the water hole again, beginning: *In two minutes he had a little fire going* ... (page 50). Notice the way it is narrated through Ripley's eyes. Imagine that you were the director of a short film of the story. Plan your sequence of shots from the moment Ripley walks towards the water hole to the moment that the puma is dead.

26 Look at this extract from just after the puma attack: ... *he crawled from under the lion like a worm, with his mouth full of grass and dirt*. What simile is used to describe Ripley? What is its effect?

27 Read the paragraph that begins: *Josefa was standing in her tracks* ... on page 51 again. What emotions is Ripley feeling at that moment? How does the story teller use the idea of the theatre to emphasize this feeling?

28 Later in the scene by the water hole, there is another comment about the theatre, in the paragraph beginning: *'Are you really sure you don't hate me?'* (page 54). How does this emphasize the way that Ripley is feeling now?

29 The story is told largely from Ripley's point of view. What new information might we expect to see in a version of the story told from Josefa's point of view?

Style

30 Look at the following extract from the start of the story, which discusses Ripley's ambition to marry Josefa. What would be a simpler way to say 'form a royal matrimonial alliance'? What would be a simpler way to say 'his magnificent qualities in the art of cattle stealing'? What is the effect of using this elevated style here?

Every cow-puncher on the range knew her by sight and was a loyal vassal. Ripley Givens, foreman of one of the Espinosa outfits, saw her one day, and made up his mind to form a royal matrimonial alliance. Presumptuous? No. In those days in the Nueces country a man was a man. And, after all, the title of cattle king does not presuppose blood royalty. Often it only signifies that its owner wears the crown in token of his magnificent qualities in the art of cattle stealing.

31 Look at the paragraph on page 49 when Ripley decides to stay the night at White Horse Crossing (*One day Ripley* ...). What do you notice about the length of the sentences. How does this mirror Ripley's decision-making process?

32 The story advises that 'It is well to be reasonably watchful when a Mexican lion sings soprano' (page 50). How does the following extract show that Ripley knows this advice?

From somewhere in the dense timber along the river came a sudden, rageful, shivering wail. The pony danced at the end of his rope and blew a whistling snort of comprehending fear. Givens puffed at his cigarette, but he reached leisurely for his pistol-belt, which lay on the grass, and twirled the cylinder of his weapon tentatively. A great gar plunged with a loud splash into the water hole. A little brown rabbit skipped around a bunch of catclaw and sat twitching his whiskers and looking humorously at Givens. The pony went on eating grass.

33 Reread the paragraph that describes how Ripley and Josefa ride back to the ranch, starting *It was now twilight*. What images emphasize the romance of the journey?

34 Read the end of the story when Josefa tells her father about shooting the puma (page 55). Compare her style of speaking with her style earlier in the story when she is sorry for having killed Bill. How do these styles differ? Is one more feminine than the other? What does this show about her character and relationship with both men?

Guidance to the above literary terms, answer keys to all the exercises and activities, plus a wealth of other reading-practice material, can be found at: www.macmillanenglish.com/readers.

The Grey Parrot
by W W Jacobs

About the author

William Wymark Jacobs was a British writer of short stories and novels. He is best known for his horror story, *The Monkey's Paw* (which you can read in the book *Horror Stories* in the Macmillan Literature Collections series). However, most of his stories were, in fact, light-hearted and funny, and describe the life of sailors and dockworkers in and around the London docks.

He was born in 1863 in East London near the river Thames. His father worked in the London docks, and he and his brothers and sisters used to spend time there watching the ships coming and going. This was to become a setting for many of his short stories, including *The Grey Parrot*. Like this story, the plots were more often about the sailors' lives on land, rather than at sea. A later collection of short stories, *Night Watches*, tells the adventures of a group of sailors as they lose all their money in the East End of London.

Jacobs studied at Birkbeck College, now a part of the University of London. When he was sixteen, he started work as a clerk in the Post Office. The job provided him with a living but it was not what he wanted to do. In his spare time, he wrote short stories.

His first short story was published in 1885. His early stories were published in smaller magazines like *The Idler* and *Today* but he didn't get his big break until 1895, when a more famous magazine, *The Strand*, decided to publish one of his stories. Within a year he was able to publish his first collection of short stories, *Many Cargoes*, and by 1899 he was earning enough from his story writing to leave his job at the Post Office. In 1900 he married Agnes Eleanor Williams, a famous suffragette, who took part in public protests to give women the right to vote. They had five children.

In the last few decades of his life he wrote very few stories, preferring instead to write adaptations of his stories for the theatre. He died in 1943 just before his 80th birthday. During his lifetime he was successful and quite well known, though he was a shy man and did not enjoy public attention. After his death, his work was largely forgotten, except for *The Monkey's Paw*, which has been adapted for theatre and cinema several times, including a movie made in 2013.

About the story

The Grey Parrot was published in 1898 in a collection of short stories called *Sea Urchins*. This was published in the United States under the name *More Cargoes*.

Background information

Life on board ship and on the docks

At the time that Jacobs was writing, the only way to travel long distances was by sea, which meant that ports were an extremely important part of the economic life of major cities. Around the end of the 19th century, steam was overtaking sail power because it was much faster at carrying large amounts of cargo for long distances. The ports of London, like the East India Docks where the story is set, were no longer populated with sailing ships, but were now dominated by steamers. Steam ships were given the prefix 'SS' in front of their name. For example, the ship in this story is called the SS *Curlew*.

The successful running of a ship requires a clear system for organizing the people on board according to their level of responsibility. On steam ships, the person in overall command of the ship was still the captain but the steam engine and the mechanical parts of the ship were the responsibility of the Chief Engineer. Below him were the Second and Third Engineers, often referred to simply as the 'Second' and 'Third'. Further down the hierarchy were many specific jobs. Apprentices were young men who worked for low pay in order to learn a profession. The men on board needed food, clean clothes and so on, so other jobs of low responsibility included working in the kitchen and washrooms. A steward, for example, was a man whose job was to serve the crew with food and drink.

Talking birds

Many species of bird can mimic, or copy, the spoken language of humans. These include large parrots and corvids (birds related to crows), as well as smaller species such as parakeets, budgerigars and myna birds. Grey parrots come from Africa and have been kept as pets for centuries because of their curious ability to speak, possibly as far back as Greek and Roman times.

The linguistic ability of birds is well known and documented. A budgerigar named Puck holds the record in the Guinness World Records for the largest vocabulary; he was able to say 1728 different words. Bibi, a Congo African grey parrot, can use greetings in 20 languages to say 'hello' and can count in six languages. She has been named 'the Polyglot Parrot'. In Australia, cockatoos that lived with humans before escaping from captivity have taught words to their new flocks of cockatoo, so there are now wild birds that speak English!

As well as being able to say words, there is a great deal of evidence that suggests a surprising level of intelligence in some of these species. Grey parrots have been shown to understand the meaning of the words they say and even to create simple sentences of their own.

Summary

It may help you to know something about what happens in the story before you read it. Don't worry, this summary does not tell you how the story ends!

The SS *Curlew* is in port at the East India Docks in London. Chief Engineer Gannet is talking with Rogers, the Third Engineer, about a parrot that Gannett has bought for his young wife. Since he has had it, though, he has discovered that it uses a lot of bad language, so he is not sure whether it will be a suitable present for Mrs Gannett. He is also worried about his wife being alone for so long when he is away at sea; he is suspicious of other men paying her attention. He tells Rogers of a plan he has to make sure that Mrs Gannett behaves while he is away. He will tell her that the parrot is magic and will be able to tell him everything she has done when he returns. Rogers does not think she will believe such a silly story.

Gannett takes the parrot home in a cage to his wife. He tells her the story that the parrot has magic powers. They then go to the theatre, but have to leave because Mr Gannett gets jealous when other men pay too much attention to his wife. The following morning, he has to go back to the ship to prepare for the ship's departure, but he will see Mrs Gannett again before the ship sets sail, when she comes on board ship that afternoon to say goodbye.

While Mrs Gannett is at home, she has a visit from a friend, Mrs Cluffins. Mrs Cluffins is interested in the parrot but shocked that Mr Gannett would tell his wife such silly stories. She accompanies Mrs Gannett to the ship and comes on board. While the couple are saying goodbye, Mrs Cluffins talks with another sailor, Jenkins, with whom she seems very friendly. The women have to get off the ship because the ship is going to leave. They watch from the dock as it disappears down the river.

In the following weeks, Mrs Gannett is bored without her husband. The parrot's language is so bad that she puts it in the spare room with a cloth over the cage to stop it from making a noise. The only enjoyment in her life are regular visits from Mrs Cluffins. Her friend suggests selling the parrot to a local pub owner, Hobson, but Mrs Gannett refuses to consider the idea; she does not want to make her husband angry.

A week before the SS *Curlew* is due to return, Mrs Cluffins finally persuades her friend to sell the parrot. But won't Mr Gannett be angry and suspicious? And why would Mrs Gannett change her mind? The answers lie in Mrs Cluffin's clever plan.

Pre-reading activities

Key vocabulary

This section will help you familiarize yourself with some of the more specific vocabulary used in the story. You may want to use it to help you before you start reading, or as a revision exercise after you have finished the story.

Ways of speaking

Much of the story is told through the dialogues that the main characters, Mr and Mrs Gannet, have with their friends and with each other. The writer tells us not only what they say directly but also the way that they say it. The parrot is another character with a voice; the way it speaks is also described.

1 **Read the sentences. Look at the words in bold. Which are: a) verbs, b) adjectives, c) nouns, and d) adverbs?**

1 We shouted so much at the football match that our voices were **hoarse** for two days.

2 He said, with a **sepulchral** tone that reminded her of an old judge, 'You have disappointed me one too many times, Fiona.'

3 She asked **prettily**, 'Could I have another cake, please, Uncle?' How could I refuse?

4 Mr McGraw pointed out, 'You might use **coarse** language like that at home, but not here.'

5 The waiter showed his usual **impudence**, grunting at me when I stepped inside and not even offering to take my coat.

6 He thought the subject of the meeting was trivial but he spoke about it with the **gravity** that was expected of a senior member of the police force.

7 He said something **feebly**. 'Speak up!' I demanded, getting increasingly frustrated by his lack of communication skills.

8 I'm sure if you tell them **boldly** enough that it's your camera they'll believe you.

9 She noticed Grandpa **raving** in the corner. I reassured her that this was perfectly normal and that she shouldn't worry about him, he'd fall asleep after a while.

10 'Gh-ghosts?' he **stammered**. 'Are there really ghosts in Awdrey Manor?'

11 The captain offered to tell them another story about the war. He didn't notice the **sarcasm** in Michael's voice when he said, 'Oh, go on. We always love hearing your stories.'

12 He denied taking the money with a **vehemence** that told me he was definitely hiding something.

13 He launched a **scathing** attack on the Prime Minister.

2 Match the words in bold in the sentences (1–13) in exercise 1 with their definitions (a–m) below.

a) a serious attitude

b) extremely strong feeling or belief

c) in a confident way, not afraid of people

d) in a way that is attractive and delicate

e) in a way that is not strong enough to be heard clearly

f) language which is like this is rude and offensive

g) *literary*: sad and serious

h) someone who has a voice which is like this speaks in a low rough voice, usually because their throat is sore

i) speaking in a rude way that shows no respect for someone

j) the activity of saying the opposite of what you mean, or of speaking in a way intended to make someone else feel stupid

k) keep repeating a sound and to have difficulty in saying certain words because of a speech problem, nervousness or excitement

l) extremely critical

m) talk in an angry and uncontrolled way

Body language

Accompanying the dialogues is a great deal of information about the gestures and physical actions that accompany speech. Often, these tell us as much about what the speakers mean as the words.

3 Find the body parts in <u>nine</u> of the extracts below.

1 Mr Gannett, … *thumping the table with his **clenched** fist, forbade his wife to mention the word again.*

2 *'If he has any of his nonsense while I'm away …,' said the Chief passionately. 'I shall know of it.'*
*The other **raised his eyebrows**.*

3 *Mrs Gannett **shook her head**. 'The house wouldn't hold my husband if I did,' she remarked with a **shiver**.*

4 Mrs Gannett, **wrinkling** her forehead, eyed the marvellous bird curiously.

5 Mrs Gannett **tossed her head** … so decidedly that a passing stranger turned his head and looked at her.

6 'I shall think of you every minute,' said the engineer … He **sighed** gently …

7 The Chief **shrugged his shoulders** disdainfully.

8 'But you don't believe it?' said his wife, **staring** at him open-mouthed.

9 Mrs Gannett nodded, 'He's awfully jealous of me,' she said with a slight **simper**.

10 'You must have given him some encouragement,' said Mr Gannett fiercely – '**made eyes at** him or something.'

11 'You'd better pour yourself out another cup,' he said thoughtfully as he **caught the Third's eye**.

12 'I should hope that he has forgotten that nonsense,' said Mrs Gannett, **reddening**.

4 If you don't already know the meaning of the words in bold in the extracts in exercise 3, try to guess them from the context. Then check your ideas with the definitions below.

---

catch someone's eyes PHRASE look at someone at the same time as they are looking at you, often used as a signal to do something or to pass on an unspoken message

clench (v) close (a part of your body) tightly, especially because you are angry or upset

make eyes at someone PHRASE look at someone in a way that shows you are attracted to them

raise your eyebrows PHRASE lift your eyebrows to a higher position, often done to show surprise or disbelief

redden (v) become red in the face because you are embarrassed, angry, or hot

shake your head PHRASE say no by turning your head from side to side

shiver (n) a shaking movement that your body makes when you are cold or frightened

shrug your shoulders PHRASE move your shoulders up and let them drop to show that you do not know something or do not care

sigh (v) breathe out slowly making a long soft sound, especially because you are disappointed, tired, annoyed, relaxed, or to show affection

simper (n) a smile that is not sincere, used when someone is pretending to be shy or modest

stare (v) look at someone or something very directly for a long time

toss your head PHRASE move your head quickly upwards, especially when you are angry or do not care about something

wrinkle (v) move part of your face so that small lines appear on it

---

5 Read the extracts in exercise 3 again. Think about the possible emotions that they may be describing.

Coming into port

6 Read the definitions for words to do with ports, then choose the correct word to complete the paragraph below.

> **ashore** (adv) on land and not on the sea
> **gangway** (n) a flat board or metal structure that can be put in place between a ship and land to let people get off or on the ship
> **harbour** (n) an area of water near the land where it is safe for boats to stay
> **pier** (n) a structure over water built out from the land where people can go to walk
> **quay** (n) a structure on the shore of a harbour where boats can stay
> **seafaring** (adj) working or travelling regularly on the sea

(1)......................... men and women look forward to the short periods of time they spend (2)........................., to visit their families and enjoy some freedom away from their superior officers. After weeks or months at sea, it's an exciting moment for them when their ship finally sails into (3)........................... Some may be able to see their families waving at them from the end of a (4).......................... as they sail past. Finally the ship moors against the (5)......................... and the (6).......................... is lowered so that they can step off the ship.

Adverbs

Adverbs describing speech

7 Read the definitions of the adverbs and answer the questions below.

so that	only if	in which case
because	as a consequence	(if you...) then

---

briskly doing something quickly and, in speech, only saying what is necessary

casually not involving strong feelings or emotions

composedly in a way that is calm but careful

curtly using few words in a way that shows you are impatient or angry

dryly (drily) in a way that expresses humour while appearing to be serious

earnestly being serious, determined, and meaning what you say

effusively expressing happiness in an extremely enthusiastic way

gravely speaking in a way that is very serious and worried

hastily done in a hurry because you do not have much time

huskily a husky voice is deep and sounds as if you have a sore throat, often in an attractive way

jerkily speaking in a way that is broken into separate short words and sounds

peremptorily speaking rather rudely, as if you expect other people to obey you

reproachfully expressing criticism or disappointment in a way that is intended to make someone feel ashamed

solemnly speaking in a serious way

tenderly speaking in a gentle way that shows that you care about someone

wearily in a way that shows that you are very tired

Which adverb(s):

a) tell us that the person is speaking fast? (2 adverbs)

b) suggest that the person may be speaking slowly? (2 adverbs)

c) could not describe someone talking about a light-hearted subject? (4 adverbs)

d) indicate that the quality of the voice has changed? (2 adverbs)

e) suggest a negative attitude by the writer towards the speaker? (2 adverbs)

f) describes the way someone might speak to a person that they love? (1 adverb)

g) describes the way someone speaks if they want to pretend that they are not interested? (1 adverb)

h) describe a way of talking that may confuse the listener? (2 adverbs)

i) describes an overwhelmingly positive emotion? (1 adverb)

8 **Choose the best adverb to complete the sentences (1–10).**

1 'I had to sort that mess out for you. Not your smartest moment, was it?' she said *reproachfully / tenderly / effusively*.

2 'I really think we can make the project work. I really do,' he insisted *curtly / earnestly / jerkily*.

3 'I'll buy these drinks,' she announced. 'The first drinks, that is,' she added *earnestly / hastily / peremptorily*.

4 'I'm afraid there isn't much we can do at this stage. We'll just have to wait for the medicine to work,' the doctor said *gravely / hastily / huskily*.

5 'I've had a long day. I just want to get home,' he said *wearily / tenderly / reproachfully*.

6 'That is *not* what I wanted,' she replied *casually / curtly / tenderly*. 'Not at all.'

7 'They told me this morning that I'm being made redundant,' she announced *effusively / composedly / peremptorily*, making sure she didn't cry.

8 'What a brilliant party that was!' he exclaimed *composedly / effusively / solemnly*.

9 'Will you … er, I mean would you,' he started *casually / jerkily / wearily*, 'do me the, er, honour … of marrying me?'

10 'You can get me my coat,' she decided *tenderly / jerkily / peremptorily*, walking towards the door.

Main themes

Before you read the story, you may want to think about some of its main themes. The questions will help you think about the story as you are reading it for the first time. There is more discussion of the main themes in the *Literary analysis* section after the story.

Married couples

The story is about the relationship of a recently-married couple, but they are not the only married people in the story. Much of the story concerns the complexities of married life.

9 As you read the story, ask yourself the following questions:

a) How many married couples are there in the story? How long have they been married?
b) What differences are there in the way the different characters talk about their marriages?
c) What marital problems are discussed?

Telling stories and lies

Sailors are famous for telling stories of their time at sea and are known for exaggerating elements of the story for a more dramatic effect.

10 As you read the story, think about these questions:

a) Who tells lies in the story? Who do they tell them too? Why?
b) Does anybody believe the lies?
c) Is it ever convenient in the story for characters to pretend that lies are the truth or that the truth is a lie?

The Grey Parrot

by W W Jacobs

The Chief Engineer and the Third sat at tea on the S.S. *Curlew* in the East India Docks. The small and not over-clean steward having placed everything he could think of upon[1] the table, and then added everything the Chief could think of, had assiduously[2] poured out two cups of tea and withdrawn by request. The two men ate steadily, conversing between bites, and interrupted occasionally by a hoarse and sepulchral voice, the owner of which, being much exercised by the sight of the food, asked for it, prettily at first, and afterwards in a way which at least compelled attention[3].

'That's pretty good for a parrot,' said the Third critically. 'Seems to know what he's saying too. No, don't give it anything. It'll stop if you do.'

'There's no pleasure to me in listening to coarse language,' said the Chief with dignity.

He absently dipped a piece of bread and butter in the Third's tea, and losing it, chased it round and round the bottom of the cup with his finger, the Third regarding the operation with an interest and emotion which he was at first unable to understand.

'You'd better pour yourself out another cup,' he said thoughtfully as he caught the Third's eye.

'I'm going to,' said the other dryly.

'The man I bought it off,' said the Chief, giving the bird the sop[4], 'said that it was a perfectly respectable parrot and wouldn't

---

1 *old-fashioned*: on
2 *formal*: in a way that is hardworking and thorough
3 the men's conversation was interrupted by a voice which began asking for food in a nice way and then much more rudely.
4 a piece of bread dipped in a liquid. *Sop* also means something that you give to someone to make them stop causing trouble for you or asking for something more valuable.

know a bad word if it heard it. I hardly like to give it to my wife now.'

'It's no good being too particular,' said the Third, regarding the other with an **ill-concealed** grin, 'that's the worst of all you young married fellows. Seem to think your wife has got to be wrapped up in brown paper. Ten chances to one she'll be amused.'

The Chief shrugged his shoulders disdainfully. 'I bought the bird to be company for her,' he said slowly, 'she'll be very lonesome without me, Rogers.'

'How do you know?' inquired the other.

'She said so,' was the reply.

'When you've been married as long as I have,' said the Third, who having been married some fifteen years felt that their usual positions were somewhat reversed, 'you'll know that generally speaking they're glad to get rid of you.'

'What for?' demanded the Chief in a voice that Othello[5] might have envied.

'Well, you get in the way a bit,' said Rogers with secret enjoyment, 'you see you upset the arrangements. House-cleaning and all that sort of thing get interrupted. They're glad to see you back at first, and then glad to see the back of you.'

'There's wives and wives,' said the **bridegroom** tenderly.

'And mine's a good one,' said the Third, 'registered A1 at Lloyds'[6], but she don't worry about me going away. Your wife's thirty years younger than you, isn't she?'

'Twenty-five,' corrected the other shortly. 'You see, what I'm afraid of is that she'll get too much attention.'

'Well, women like that,' remarked the Third.

'But I don't, **damn it**,' cried the Chief hotly. 'When I think of it I get hot all over. Boiling hot.'

'That won't last,' said the other reassuringly, 'you won't care twopence this time next year.'

---

5 a Shakespeare character who is known for being a jealous husband

6 the Lloyds register classifies all large ships according to how well made they are; A1 is the best classification. The man is comparing his wife to a ship.

'We're not all alike,' growled the Chief, 'some of us have got finer feelings than others have. I saw the chap[7] next door looking at her as we passed him this morning.'

'Lor[8],' said the Third.

'I don't want any of your damned impudence,' said the Chief sharply. 'He put his hat on straighter when he passed us. What do you think of that?'

'Can't say,' replied the other with commendable gravity, 'it might mean anything.'

'If he has any of his **nonsense** while I'm away I'll break his neck,' said the Chief passionately. 'I shall know of it.'

The other raised his eyebrows.

'I've asked the **landlady** to keep her eyes open a bit,' said the Chief. 'My wife was brought up in the country and she's very young and simple, so that it is quite right and proper for her to have a motherly old body to look after her.'

'Told your wife?' queried Rogers.

'No,' said the other. 'Fact is, I've got an idea about that parrot. I'm going to tell her it's a magic bird, and will tell me everything she does while I'm away. Anything the landlady tells me I shall tell her I got from the parrot. For one thing, I don't want her to go out after seven of an evening, and she's promised me she won't. If she does I shall know, and pretend that I know through the parrot. What do you think of it?'

'Think of it?' said the Third, staring at him. 'Think of it? **Fancy** a man telling a grown-up woman a **yarn** like that!'

'She believes in warnings and death-watches[9], and all that sort of thing,' said the Chief, 'so why shouldn't she?'

'Well, you'll know whether she believes in it or not when you come back,' said Rogers, 'and it'll be a great pity, because it's a beautiful talker.'

'What do you mean?' said the other.

---

7 *old-fashioned*: a man
8 'Lord', a reference to God, used for showing that you are very surprised, angry, or upset
9 a small beetle that makes a sound like a watch ticking that was believed to be a sign of death

'I mean it'll get its little neck **wrung**,' said the Third.

'Well, we'll see,' said Gannett. 'I shall know what to think if it does die.'

'I shall never see that bird again,' said Rogers, shaking his head as the Chief took up the cage and handed it to the steward, who was to accompany him home with it.

The couple left the ship and proceeded down the East India Dock Road side by side, the only incident being a hot argument between a constable[10] and the engineer as to whether he could or could not be held responsible for the language in which the parrot **saw fit** to indulge when the steward happened to drop it.

The engineer took the cage at his door, and, not without some **misgivings**, took it upstairs into the parlour[11] and set it on the table. Mrs Gannett, a simple-looking woman, with sleepy brown eyes and a docile manner, clapped her hands with joy.

'Isn't it a beauty?' said Mr Gannett, looking at it; 'I bought it to be company for you while I'm away.'

'You're too good to me, Jem,' said his wife. She walked all round the cage admiring it, and the parrot, which was of a hugely suspicious and nervous **disposition**, having had boys at its last place, turning with her. After she had walked round him five times he got sick of it, and in a simple sailorly fashion said so.

'Oh, Jem,' said his wife.

'It's a beautiful talker,' said Gannett hastily, 'and it's so clever that it picks up everything it hears, but it'll soon forget it.'

'It looks as though it knows what you are saying,' said his wife. 'Just look at it, the **artful** thing.'

The opportunity was too good to be missed, and in a few straightforward lies the engineer acquainted[12] Mrs Gannett of the miraculous powers with which he had chosen to endow[13] it.

'But you don't believe it?' said his wife, staring at him open-mouthed.

10 in the UK, a police officer of the lowest rank
11 *old-fashioned*: a room in a house, used for entertaining guests
12 *formal*: to give someone information about something
13 *formal*: to give something a particular quality

'I do,' said the engineer firmly.

'But how can it know what I'm doing when I'm away?' persisted Mrs Gannett.

'Ah, that's its secret,' said the engineer; 'a good many people would like to know that, but nobody has found out yet. It's a magic bird, and when you've said that, you've said all there is to say about it.'

Mrs Gannett, wrinkling her forehead, eyed the marvellous bird curiously.

'You'll find it's quite true,' said Gannett; 'when I come back that bird'll be able to tell me how you've been and all about you. Everything you've done during my absence.'

'Good gracious![14],' said the astonished Mrs Gannett.

'If you stay out after seven of an evening, or do anything else that I shouldn't like, that bird'll tell me,' continued the engineer impressively. 'It'll tell me who comes to see you, and in fact it will tell me everything you do while I'm away.'

'Well, it won't have anything bad to tell of me,' said Mrs Gannett composedly, 'unless it tells lies.'

'It can't tell lies,' said her husband confidently, 'and now, if you go and put your **bonnet** on, we'll drop in at the theatre for half an hour.'

It was a **prophetic** utterance[15], for he made such a fuss over the man next to his wife, offering her his **opera-glasses**, that they left, at the urgent request of the management, in almost exactly that space of time.

'You'd better carry me about in a band-box[16],' said Mrs Gannett wearily as the outraged engineer **stalked** home beside her. 'What harm was the man doing?'

'You must have given him some encouragement,' said Mr Gannett fiercely – 'made eyes at him or something. A man wouldn't offer to lend a lady his opera-glasses without.'

---

14 used for showing that you are very surprised, angry, or upset
15 *formal*: a statement
16 *old-fashioned*: a light box that was used to carry light clothing and keep it clean and neat

Mrs Gannett tossed her head – and that so decidedly, that a passing stranger turned his head and looked at her. Mr Gannett accelerated his pace, and taking his wife's arm, led her swiftly home with a passion too great for words.

By the morning his anger had evaporated, but his misgivings remained. He left after breakfast for the *Curlew*, which was to sail in the afternoon, leaving behind him **copious** instructions, by following which his wife would be enabled to come down and see him off with the minimum exposure of her fatal **charms**.

Left to herself Mrs Gannett dusted the room, until coming to the parrot's cage she put down the duster and eyed its **eerie** occupant curiously. She fancied that she saw an evil glitter in the creature's eye, and the knowing way in which it drew the film[17] over it was as near an approach to a wink as a bird could get.

She was still looking at it when there was a knock at the door, and a bright little woman – rather smartly dressed – **bustled** into the room, and greeted her effusively.

'I just come to see you, my dear, because I thought a little outing would do me good,' she said briskly; 'and if you've no objection I'll come down to the docks with you to see the boat off.'

Mrs Gannett assented readily. It would ease the engineer's mind, she thought, if he saw her with a chaperon[18].

'Nice bird,' said Mrs Cluffins, mechanically, bringing her **parasol** to the charge.

'Don't do that,' said her friend hastily.

'Why not?' said the other.

'Language!' said Mrs Gannett solemnly.

'Well, I must do something to it,' said Mrs Cluffins restlessly.

She held the parasol near the cage and suddenly opened it. It was a flaming **scarlet**, and for a moment the shock took the parrot's breath away.

'He don't mind[19] that,' said Mrs Gannett.

---

17 birds have an extra eyelid, which is a thin layer, or film, that covers the eye.

18 *old-fashioned*: an older woman who went with a young unmarried woman to social events

19 *unusual*: he doesn't care for that, or like it.

The parrot, hopping to the farthest corner of the bottom of his cage, said something feebly. Finding that nothing dreadful happened, he repeated his remark somewhat more boldly, and, being convinced after all that the apparition was quite harmless and that he had displayed his craven[20] spirit for nothing, hopped back on his perch and raved wickedly.

'If that was my bird,' said Mrs Cluffins, almost as scarlet as her parasol, 'I should wring its neck.'

'No, you wouldn't,' said Mrs Gannett solemnly. And having quieted the bird by throwing a cloth over its cage, she explained its properties.

'What!' said Mrs Cluffins, unable to sit still in her chair. 'You mean to tell me your husband said that!'

Mrs Gannett nodded, 'He's awfully jealous of me,' she said with a slight simper.

'I wish he was my husband,' said Mrs Cluffins in a thin, hard voice. 'I wish C.[21] would talk to me like that. I wish somebody would try and persuade C. to talk to me like that.'

'It shows he's fond of me,' said Mrs Gannett, looking down.

Mrs Cluffins jumped up and snatched the cover off the cage; endeavoured, but in vain, to get the parasol through the bars.

'And you believe that rubbish!' she said scathingly. 'Boo, you wretch[22]!'

'I don't believe it,' said her friend, taking her gently away and covering the cage hastily just as the bird was recovering, 'but I let him think I do.'

'I call it an **outrage**,' said Mrs Cluffins, waving the parasol wildly. 'I never heard of such a thing; I'd like to give Mr Gannett a piece of my mind. Just about half an hour of it. He wouldn't be the same man afterwards – I'd parrot[23] him.'

---

20 *formal*: not brave
21 referring to her husband, Mr Cluffin
22 *humorous*: someone who you do not like or who annoys you (she is talking to the bird)
23 *to parrot* means to copy what someone says, but here the noun 'parrot' is used as a verb to show that Mrs Cluffins is angry with Mr Gannett and would like to tell him that she disapproves of his story.

Mrs Gannett, **soothing** her agitated friend as well as she was able, led her gently to a chair and removed her bonnet, and finding that complete recovery was impossible while the parrot remained in the room, took that wonder-working bird outside.

By the time they had reached the docks and boarded the *Curlew* Mrs Cluffins had quite recovered her spirits. She roamed about the steamer asking questions, which savoured more of idle curiosity than a genuine thirst for knowledge[24], and was **at no pains** to conceal her opinion of those who were unable to **furnish** her with satisfactory replies.

'I shall think of you every day, Jem,' said Mrs Gannett tenderly.

'I shall think of you every minute,' said the engineer reproachfully.

He sighed gently and gazed in a scandalised fashion at Mrs Cluffins, who was carrying on a desperate flirtation with one of the apprentices.

'She's very light-hearted,' said his wife, following the direction of his eyes.

'She is,' said Mr Gannett curtly, as the **unconscious** Mrs Cluffins shut her parasol and rapped the apprentice playfully with the handle. 'She seems to be on very good terms with Jenkins, laughing and carrying on. I don't suppose she's ever seen him before.'

'Poor young things,' said Mrs Cluffins solemnly, as she came up to them. 'Don't you worry, Mr Gannett; I'll look after her and keep her from **moping**.'

'You're very kind,' said the engineer slowly.

'We'll have a jolly time,' said Mrs Cluffins. 'I often wish my husband was a seafaring man. A wife does have more freedom, doesn't she?'

'More what?' inquired Mr Gannett huskily.

'More freedom,' said Mrs Cluffins gravely. 'I always envy sailors' wives. They can do as they like. No husband to look after them for nine or ten months in the year.'

---

24 her questions show that she is not genuinely interested in the answers.

Before the unhappy engineer could put his **indignant** thoughts into words there was a warning cry from the gangway, and, with a hasty farewell, he hurried below. The visitors went ashore, the gangway was shipped, and in response to the clang of the telegraph[25], the *Curlew* drifted slowly away from the quay and headed for the spring bridge slowly opening in front of her.

The two ladies hurried to the pier-head and watched the steamer down the river until a bend hid it from view. Then Mrs Gannett, with a sensation of having lost something, due, so her friend assured her, to the **want** of a cup of tea, went slowly back to her lonely home.

In the period of grass widowhood[26] which ensued, Mrs Cluffins' visits formed almost the sole relief to the bare **monotony** of existence. As a companion the parrot was an utter failure, its language being so **irredeemably** bad that it spent most of its time in the spare room with a cloth over its cage, wondering when the days were going to lengthen a bit. Mrs Cluffins suggested selling it, but her friend repelled the suggestion with horror, and refused to entertain it at any price, even that of the publican[27] at the corner, who, having heard of the bird's command of language, was **bent** upon buying it.

'I wonder what that beauty will have to tell your husband,' said Mrs Cluffins, as they sat together one day some three months after the *Curlew*'s departure.

'I should hope that he has forgotten that nonsense,' said Mrs Gannett, reddening; 'he never alludes[28] to it in his letters.'

'Sell it,' said Mrs Cluffins peremptorily. 'It's no good to you, and Hobson would give anything for it almost.'

Mrs Gannett shook her head. 'The house wouldn't hold my husband if I did,' she remarked with a shiver.

---

25 on steam ships, a telegraph was a communications device that the captain used to tell the engine room to power the ship at a particular speed. It made a bell ring with a 'clanging' sound.

26 *old-fashioned*: a woman whose husband is away for a long time was known as a 'grass widow'.

27 *British English*: someone who owns or manages a pub

28 *formal*: to mention something in an indirect way

'Oh, yes it would,' said Mrs Cluffins; 'you do as I tell you, and a much smaller house than this would hold him. I told C. to tell Hobson he should have it for five pounds.'

'But he mustn't,' said her friend in alarm.

'Leave yourself right in my hands,' said Mrs Cluffins, spreading out two small palms, and regarding them complacently. 'It'll be all right, I promise you.'

She put her arm round her friend's waist and led her to the window, talking earnestly. In five minutes Mrs Gannett was **wavering**, in ten she had **given way**, and in fifteen the energetic Mrs Cluffins was *en route* for Hobson's, swinging the cage so violently in her excitement that the parrot was reduced to holding on to its perch with claws and bill. Mrs Gannett watched the progress from the window, and with a queer[29] look on her face sat down to think out the points of attack and defence in the approaching **fray**.

A week later a four-wheeler drove up to the door, and the engineer, darting upstairs three steps at a time, dropped an armful of parcels on the floor, and caught his wife in an **embrace** which would have done credit to a bear. Mrs Gannett, for reasons of which a lack of muscle was only one, responded less ardently[30].

'Ha, it's good to be home again,' said Gannett, sinking into an easy-chair and pulling his wife on his knee. 'And how have you been? Lonely?'

'I got used to it,' said Mrs Gannett softly.

The engineer coughed. 'You had the parrot,' he remarked.

'Yes, I had the magic parrot,' said Mrs Gannett.

'How's it getting on?' said her husband, looking round. 'Where is it?'

'Part of it is on the mantelpiece,' said Mrs Gannett, trying to speak calmly, 'part of it is in a bonnet-box upstairs, some of it's in my pocket, and here is the remainder.'

She fumbled in her pocket and placed in his hand a cheap two-bladed **clasp knife**.

29 *old-fashioned*: strange
30 *literary*: showing very strong feelings of love towards someone

'On the mantelpiece?' repeated the engineer, staring at the knife; 'in a bonnet-box!'

'Those blue vases,' said his wife.

Mr Gannett put his hand to his head. If he had heard aright[31] one parrot had changed into a pair of vases, a bonnet, and a knife. A magic bird **with a vengeance**.

'I sold it,' said Mrs Gannett suddenly.

The engineer's knee stiffened inhospitably, and his arm dropped from his wife's waist. She rose quietly and took a chair opposite.

'Sold it!' said Mr Gannett in awful tones. 'Sold my parrot!'

'I didn't like it, Jem,' said his wife. 'I didn't want that bird watching me, and I did want the vases, and the bonnet, and the little present for you.'

Mr Gannett **pitched** the little present into the corner of the room.

'You see it mightn't have told the truth, Jem,' continued Mrs Gannett. 'It might have told all sorts of lies about me, and made no end of **mischief**.'

'It couldn't lie,' shouted the engineer passionately, rising from his chair and pacing the room. 'It's your guilty conscience that's made a coward of you. How dare you sell my parrot?'

'Because it wasn't truthful, Jem,' said his wife, who was somewhat pale.

'If you were half as truthful you'd do,' vociferated the engineer, standing over her. 'You, you **deceitful** woman.'

Mrs Gannett fumbled in her pocket again, and producing a small **handkerchief** applied it deliberately to her eyes.

'I – I got rid of it **for your sake**,' she stammered. 'It used to tell such lies about you. I couldn't bear to listen to it.'

'About me!' said Mr Gannett, sinking into his seat and staring at his wife with very natural amazement. 'Tell lies about me! Nonsense! How could it?'

'I suppose it could tell me about you as easily as it could tell you about me?' said Mrs Gannett. 'There was more magic in that

31 *old-fashioned*: correctly

bird than you thought, Jem. It used to say shocking things about you. I couldn't bear it.'

'Do you think you're talking to a child or a fool?' demanded the engineer.

Mrs Gannett shook her head feebly. She still kept the handkerchief to her eyes, but allowed a portion to drop over her mouth.

'I should like to hear one of the stories it told about me, if you can remember them,' said the engineer with bitter sarcasm.

'The first lie,' said Mrs Gannett in a feeble but ready voice, 'was about the time you were at Genoa[32]. The parrot said you were at some concert gardens at the upper end of the town.'

One moist eye coming mildly from behind the handkerchief saw the engineer stiffen suddenly in his chair.

'I don't suppose there even is such a place,' she continued.

'I – b'leve – there – is,' said her husband jerkily. 'I've heard – our chaps – talk of it.'

'But you haven't been there?' said his wife anxiously.

'Never!' said the engineer with extraordinary vehemence.

'That wicked bird said that you got intoxicated[33] there,' said Mrs Gannett in solemn accents, 'that you smashed a little marble-topped table and knocked down two waiters, and that if it hadn't been for the captain of the *Pursuit*, who was in there and who got you away, you'd have been locked up. Wasn't it a wicked bird?'

'Horrible!' said the engineer huskily.

'I don't suppose there ever was a ship called the *Pursuit*,' continued Mrs Gannett.

'Doesn't sound like a ship's name,' murmured Mr Gannett.

'Well, then, a few days later it said the *Curlew* was at Naples.'

'I never went ashore all the time we were at Naples,' remarked the engineer casually.

'The parrot said you did,' said Mrs Gannett.

'I suppose you'll believe your own lawful husband before that damned bird?' shouted Gannett, starting up.

32 Genoa, and further down in the text, Naples, are port cities in Italy
33 *formal*: drunk

'Of course I didn't believe it, Jem,' said his wife. 'I'm trying to prove to you that the bird was not truthful, but you're so hard to persuade.'

Mr Gannett took a pipe from his pocket, and with a small knife dug with much severity and determination a hardened plug[34] from the bowl, and blew noisily through the stem.

'There was a girl kept a fruit-stall just by the harbour,' said Mrs Gannett, 'and on this evening, on the strength of having bought three-penny-worth of green figs, you put your arm round her waist and tried to kiss her, and her sweetheart, who was standing close by, tried to **stab** you. The parrot said that you were in such a state of terror that you jumped into the harbour and were nearly drowned.'

Mr Gannett having loaded his pipe lit it slowly and carefully, and with tidy precision got up and deposited the match in the fireplace.

'It used to frighten me so with its stories that I hardly knew what to do with myself,' continued Mrs Gannett. 'When you were at Suez[35] –'

The engineer waved his hand imperiously.

'That's enough,' he said stiffly.

'I'm sure I don't want to have to repeat what it told me about Suez,' said his wife. 'I thought you'd like to hear it, that's all.'

'Not at all,' said the engineer, puffing at his pipe. 'Not at all.'

'But you see why I got rid of the bird, don't you?' said Mrs Gannett. 'If it had told you untruths about me, you would have believed them, wouldn't you?'

Mr Gannett took his pipe from his mouth and took his wife in his extended arms. 'No, my dear,' he said brokenly, 'no more than you believe all this stuff about me.'

'And I did quite right to sell it, didn't I, Jem?'

'Quite right,' said Mr Gannett with a great assumption of **heartiness**. 'Best thing to do with it.'

'You haven't heard the worst yet,' said Mrs Gannett. 'When you were at Suez –'

34 a piece of old tobacco that is difficult to get out of a pipe
35 a port city in Egypt

Mr Gannett consigned Suez to its only rival, and thumping the table with his clenched fist, forbade his wife to mention the word again, and desired her to prepare supper.

Not until he heard his wife moving about in the kitchen below did he relax the severity of his countenance[36]. Then his expression changed to one of extreme anxiety, and he restlessly paced the room seeking for light. It came suddenly.

'Jenkins,' he gasped, 'Jenkins and Mrs Cluffins, and I was going to tell Cluffins about him writing to his wife, I expect he knows the letter by heart.'

36 *literary*: your face, or the expression on your face

Post-reading activities

Understanding the story

Use these questions to help you check that you have understood the story.

On board the SS Curlew

1 Why does Gannett, the Chief Engineer, feed the parrot?
2 Why does Third Engineer Rogers need to pour himself another cup of tea?
3 What was Gannett's plan for the parrot? Why is he not so sure it is a good plan now?
4 In what sense is the two men's relationship different from normal during this conversation?
5 According to Rogers, why do sailors' wives have a mixed reaction to their husbands being at home?
6 Why is Gannett anxious about his wife?
7 Why does Gannett really want to give his wife the parrot?
8 What is Rogers' opinion of the plan? What does he predict will happen?

At the Gannetts' house

9 What happens on the way home?
10 What is Mrs Gannett's initial reaction to her present?
11 Why do they leave the theatre early?
12 What 'instructions' do you think her husband gives Mrs Gannett before he leaves for work the next morning?
13 How does Mrs Cluffins frighten the bird? Why does she do it?
14 In her first conversation with Mrs Cluffins, what do we discover about Mrs Gannett's view of her husband's lie about the parrot?
15 What does Mrs Cluffins think about what Mr Gannett told his wife?

The Curlew sets sail

16 What is Mr Gannett's opinion of Mrs Cluffins?
17 Who does Mrs Cluffins talk to most on board the Curlew?
18 How does Mrs Cluffins reassure Mr Gannett? Why doesn't it work?
19 While Mr Gannett is away what is life like for Mrs Gannett? And for the parrot?
20 What is Mrs Cluffins' suggestion? Why does Mrs Gannett reject this idea?

21 When she mentions the idea again, how long does it take Mrs Cluffins to persuade her friend to change her mind?

22 What happens to the parrot?

Mr Gannett is home again

23 What has Mrs Gannett done with the money from the sale of the parrot?

24 What is Mr Gannett's reaction to the news?

25 What reason does she give for getting rid of the parrot?

26 When does his anger stop?

27 What story about Genoa does his wife say the parrot told her? Did it really happen?

28 We discover what happened in Naples but not Suez. Why is this?

29 What does Mr Gannett realize at the end of the story?

Language study

Grammar

Present and perfect participle clauses

A common structure in the story is the use of participle clauses. They are often used to add detail about the characters while they are speaking:

*'It's no good being too particular,' said the Third, **regarding the other with an ill-concealed grin.***

Participle clauses are 'reduced clauses' – they contain a verb, but they do not contain a subject.

In **present participle clauses** we use the *–ing* form of the verb. The present participle can substitute a verb in the past simple. Here is a sentence from the beginning of the story:

*He absently dipped a piece of bread and butter in the Third's tea, and **losing** it, chased it round and round the bottom of the cup with his finger, the Third **regarding** the operation with an interest and emotion which he was at first unable to understand.*

The same sentence could be written without the participles:

*He absently dipped a piece of bread and butter in the Third's tea. **He lost it and** chased it round and round the bottom of the cup with his finger. **The Third regarded** the operation with an interest and emotion which he was at first unable to understand.*

In **perfect participle clauses** we use *having* + past participle. The perfect participle is used to substitute for the past perfect and it indicates that the action has already happened, some time before the main action:

*'When you've been married as long as I have,' said the Third, who **having been married** some fifteen years felt that their usual positions were somewhat reversed.*

1 **Complete the extracts with either the present participle or perfect participle of the verbs in brackets.**

1 *'Think of it?' said the Third, ... (stare) at him.*(page 78)
2 *She walked all round the cage .... (admire) it, and the parrot, which was of a hugely suspicious and nervous disposition, ... (have) boys at its last place, ... (turn) with her.*(page 79)
3 *Left to herself Mrs Gannett dusted the room, until .... (come) to the parrot's cage she put down the duster and eyed its eerie occupant curiously.*(page 81)
4 *As a companion the parrot was an utter failure, its language .... (be) so irredeemably bad that it spent most of its time in the spare room with a cloth over its cage.*(page 84)
5 *Mrs Cluffins suggested selling it, but her friend refused … to entertain it at any price, even that of the publican at the corner, who, ... (hear) of the bird's command of language, was bent upon buying it.*(page 84)
6 *'About me!' said Mr Gannett, ... (sink) into his seat and .... (stare) at his wife with very natural amazement.*(page 86)

Check your answers in the story by using the page references.

Vocabulary

Idiomatic expressions

2 **Look at the idiomatic expressions from the story (1–9) and match them with their definitions (a–i).**

1 keep one's eyes open
Mr Gannett is explaining his plan to Rogers:
*'I've asked the landlady to **keep her eyes open** a bit,' said the Chief.*

2 follow the direction of someone's eye
   The Gannetts watch Mrs Cluffins talking to the sailors:
   *'She's very light-hearted,' said his wife, **following the direction of his
   eyes**.*

3 see the back of someone
   Rogers is explaining wives' attitude to their husbands:
   *They're glad to see you back at first, and then glad to **see the back of
   you**.*

4 see someone or something off
   Mrs Cluffins offers to accompany Mrs Gannett to the boat:
   *I'll come down to the docks with you to **see the boat off**.*

5 leave/put something in someone's hands
   Mrs Cluffins wants Mrs Gannett to trust her to help her:
   ***'Leave yourself right in my hands**,' said Mrs Cluffins ... 'It'll be all
   right, I promise you.'*

6 ease one's mind
   Mrs Cluffins is offering to accompany her to the ship:
   *It would **ease the engineer's mind**, she thought, if he saw her with a
   chaperon.*

7 give someone a piece of your mind
   Mrs Cluffins is angry with Mr Gannett:
   *I'd like to **give Mr Gannett a piece of my mind**.*

8 take someone's breath away
   Mrs Cluffins is provoking the parrot with her parasol:
   *For a moment the shock **took the parrot's breath away**.*

9 know something by heart
   Mr Gannett realizes that Mr Cluffins has read the letter many times:
   *I expect he **knows the letter by heart**.*

a) tell someone what you think of them, especially when you are angry
b) surprise someone so they can't say anything
c) go somewhere in order to say goodbye to someone
d) watch someone secretly so that you know what they do, especially
   when you are doing something else
e) look to see what someone else is looking at
f) make someone feel less worried
g) allow someone to be responsible for dealing with something
h) be pleased when someone is no longer around
i) remember all the words in something without any help

3 **Match the sentence halves (1–9) with the endings (a–i).**

1 I can't believe her attitude. Some of the things she says just
2 I have to go out for the afternoon but if I leave the shop
3 Ooh, I'm so angry! If I could speak to her, I'd
4 She felt stupid. The rest of the class seemed to understand it perfectly. So she decided to
5 If you want I can come with you to the station to
6 I've just about had enough of that woman. I'll be pleased to
7 The nurse could see her walking back and forth anxiously so he went over to
8 She stared down, looking terrified. Afraid of what I might see, I had to
9 I know you're busy, but it's important we find out who's stealing from the office. I'm sure you could

a) ease her mind a little.
b) follow the direction of her eyes.
c) give her a piece of my mind.
d) learn the whole chapter by heart.
e) keep your eyes open for me.
f) in her hands, I'm sure there won't be problems.
g) see the back of her.
h) see you off.
i) take my breath away.

Literary analysis

Plot

1 The story begins on board the *Curlew*. Where does most of the story take place? When do we hear about Gannett's life at sea again?
2 Here are some of the events in the story. Put them in chronological order (the order in which they happened).
   Mr Gannett buys the parrot.
   Mr Gannett gives his wife the parrot.
   Mr Gannett returns home.
   Mrs Gannett sells the parrot.
   The ship sets sail again.
   The parrot learns some rude words.
   The ship stops at Genoa.
   The ship stops at Naples.

3   Look at the list again. Can you add any more key events?
4   Why is Mrs Cluffins important in the story?
5   To Mrs Gannett, is what happened in Naples better or worse than
    Genoa? What do you think happened in Suez?
6   In the final paragraph, Mr Gannett realizes that Mr Cluffins has
    probably read the letter Jenkins sent to Mrs Cluffins. What was Mr
    Gannett going to do about this letter? Why?
7   What does the story tell us about trust?
8   Do you think Mr and Mrs Gannett's relationship will change in any
    way because of the parrot?

Character

 9   What are Mr Gannett's main personal qualities?
10   Do you sympathize with him; that is, do you like him, care about
     him, or feel his emotions in any way? Why? Why not?
11   What sort of person is Mrs Gannett? What does her reaction to
     Mrs Cluffins' plan tell us about her?
12   Read again the final dialogue between husband and wife. What
     gestures and comments tell us that she is acting and is in control of
     her emotions and reactions?
13   What do you know about Mrs Cluffins? Think about her age and
     her personality. Choose three adjectives to describe her.
14   When do you think Mrs Cluffins started to plan to help her friend?
     What does her plan tell you about her?
15   Do the two marital relationships (the Gannetts' and the Cluffins')
     conform to any stereotypes about married couples that you
     know of?

Animals in the story

16   Which of the following roles does the parrot fulfil in the story?
     Who sees it in these ways?
     a present
     a spy
     an annoyance
     a thing of curiosity and entertainment
     a thing of value

17   What cruelty to the parrot is described in the story? Why are
     people cruel to it?

18 Read this extract, and think about the way in which the parrot is being described:

Left to herself Mrs Gannett dusted the room, until coming to the parrot's cage she put down the duster and eyed its eerie occupant curiously. She fancied that she saw an evil glitter in the creature's eye, and the knowing way in which it drew the film over it was as near an approach to a wink as a bird could get.

Is there any evidence to suggest that the parrot is 'evil' and 'knowing'? Why is it described this way?

19 Are there any other moments in the story when we are told about the parrot as if it had human-like emotions and motives?

20 How does the story teller prevent us from seeing the parrot as a character in the story, with thoughts and feelings of its own?

21 In the following extracts, find words to describe the parrot. What do these words suggest about the parrot? Are they true? What is the effect of describing the parrot like this?

a) *The opportunity was too good to be missed, and in a few straightforward lies the engineer acquainted Mrs Gannett of the miraculous powers with which he had chosen to endow it.*

b) *Mrs Gannett … led [Mrs Cluffins] gently to a chair and removed her bonnet, and finding that complete recovery was impossible while the parrot remained in the room, took that wonder-working bird outside.*

c) *The engineer coughed. 'You had the parrot,' he remarked. 'Yes, I had the magic parrot,' said Mrs Gannett.*

Narration

22 A lot of the story is told through the dialogues between characters. Things that could be told in the storyteller's voice are told in the characters' voices instead. In the two extracts below, what do we learn about Mrs Cluffins through what she says?

a) *'Well, I must do something to it'* (Mrs Cluffins is poking her parasol at the parrot and Mrs Gannett tells her not to)

b) *'We'll have a jolly time … I often wish my husband was a seafaring man. A wife does have more freedom, doesn't she? … I always envy sailors' wives. They can do as they like. No husband to look after them for nine or ten months in the year.'* (Mrs Cluffins is talking to Mr Gannett on board the *Curlew*)

From the following extract, what do we learn about Rogers from what he says?

   c) (Mr Gannett has just told Rogers his plan with the parrot and asks him for his opinion) *'Think of it?' said the Third, staring at him. 'Think of it? Fancy a man telling a grown-up woman a yarn like that!'*

23   Find more extracts where a character's words show us something about their personality. What do they say about them?

24   We know that the parrot uses all sorts of bad language, but we are never told what the parrot says directly. Instead, euphemisms are used. A euphemism is a word or expression that people use when they want to talk about something unpleasant or embarrassing without mentioning the thing itself. In the case above, it is easy to understand what the storyteller means when he says *'the language in which the parrot saw fit to indulge'*, and it is also understandable why he avoids the bad language.

   Look at the following extracts and identify the euphemisms:

   a) *[The parrot] asked for it, prettily at first, and afterwards in a way which at least compelled attention.*
   b) *... having heard of the bird's command of language ...*
   c) *After she had walked round him five times he got sick of it, and in a simple sailorly fashion said so.*

25   Do similar techniques to avoid swear words or difficult subjects exist in your language? Do you find the euphemisms in the story funny? Too careful? Silly? Difficult to understand?

26   Look again at the conversation between Gannett and Rogers, before Gannett tells him the plan to fool his wife. Gannett is taking the conversation very seriously, but it is amusing Rogers. Gannett is his boss, so he can't laugh at him openly. Find comments where the story teller is letting us into the secret that Rogers is silently laughing at Gannett.

27   At the end of the story, Mr Gannett suddenly realizes the way his wife has found out about his embarrassing moments. Is the ending improved by being told this? How else could it have ended?

Style

28   Read the beginning of the story again. What is the first mention of the parrot? When are we told that it is a parrot? What is the effect of not knowing straight away?

29   There is a lot of dialogue in the story but some dialogues are not reported in full. Instead, they are summarized by the story teller, such as this one:

> *The couple left the ship and proceeded down the East India Dock Road side by side, the only incident being a hot argument between a constable and the engineer as to whether he could or could not be held responsible for the language in which the parrot saw fit to indulge when the steward happened to drop it.*

Write the dialogue reported in the sentence above as you imagine it was said.

30   Compare your dialogue with the sentence. How would you describe the style of the sentence in the story? What is the effect?

31   Find the other example of a dialogue that is not reported in full, which takes place at the theatre (page 80). What does this summary have in common with the one in question 29?

Understatement

Some of the more comical scenes between characters are described with less emotion than they might be. In the following extract, think about how the Third, Rogers, must be feeling watching Gannett drop bread in his tea and put his fingers in it. Compare this with the way that it is told:

> *He absently dipped a piece of bread and butter in the Third's tea, and losing it, chased it round and round the bottom of the cup with his finger, the Third regarding the operation with an interest and emotion which he was at first unable to understand.*
>
> *'You'd better pour yourself out another cup,' he said thoughtfully as he caught the Third's eye.*
>
> *'I'm going to,' said the other dryly.*

Notice the change in style, from a neutral style: 'chased it round and round the bottom of the cup with his finger', to more formal and impersonal: 'regarding the operation with an interest and emotion which he was at first unable to understand.'

32   Now look at another extract. Identify the change of style by underlining the more formal, impersonal part of the sentence. How is Mrs Gannett feeling? How is this conveyed here?

The engineer … caught his wife in an embrace which would have done credit to a bear. Mrs Gannett, for reasons of which a lack of muscle was only one, responded less ardently.

33   Find another example of understatement in the story.

Guidance to the above literary terms, answer keys to all the exercises and activities, plus a wealth of other reading-practice material, can be found at: www.macmillanenglish.com/readers.

Lappin and Lapinova
by Virginia Woolf

About the author

Virginia Stephen was born in London in 1882 into a large Victorian family. Her mother and father had four children from previous marriages. Virginia was the third of four more children that Leslie and Julia Stephen had together. Along with seven servants and numerous guests that visited regularly, they made a busy and noisy household in the fashionable district of Kensington in West London.

Sir Leslie Stephen was a successful writer and editor of dictionaries and biographies. Through him, the family were friends with many well-known authors, including George Eliot, Alfred Tennyson and Henry James. The family went on holiday to St Ives in Cornwall every summer; this is where some of Woolf's happiest memories come from. She brings the seaside experiences into some of her most famous works, such as the novel *To the Lighthouse*. She also used to play cricket there with the young Rupert Brooke, who became a famous poet of the First World War.

Her two brothers, Thoby and Adrian, were sent to school and, later, Cambridge University, but in those days it was unusual for girls to be given a formal education. Instead Virginia and her sister, Vanessa, were taught at home by their parents. Woolf really missed the academic life; she realized how unfair it was that women were treated differently to men early in life. She returns to this theme many times in her letters and essays, most famously in *A Room of One's Own*, which is generally regarded as a feminist text. Their parents were not very good teachers to the girls, so they educated themselves. At a young age, Vanessa decided to become an artist and Virginia wanted to become a writer. They realized these ambitions, Vanessa going on to become an accomplished artist and illustrator, and Virginia becoming an author and one of the leading modernists of the 20th century. Her work is still read and studied today.

Woolf's feminist ideals were extremely unconventional for the time in which she lived. She actively questioned many aspects of life and she was experimental with many things, from her writing to her private life. In 1904, after their father died, the Stephen children, now in their twenties, moved to a different district of London called Bloomsbury. There, male friends of their brothers from Cambridge, as well as other writers, painters and intellectuals, met and discussed a wide range of issues such as art, politics and society. They challenged and rejected many things that other people living at that time didn't think to question. The 'Bloomsbury Group', as it was later called, was united by its belief in the importance of the arts, and the Group's work and outlook went on to influence literature, as well as modern attitudes towards feminism.

Woolf experienced a number of tragedies throughout her life. Her mother died when she was 13 years old. Soon afterwards, she suffered her first mental breakdown, the first of many. Her depression was deeper when her father died nine years later; she even tried to kill herself on that occasion. While her brother Thoby was on holiday in Greece in 1906, he caught typhoid and died. Depression was becoming more and more a part of her life. It entered her writing as well. She is admired for her literary descriptions of madness and her exposure of the instability of her characters' minds.

In 1912, Virginia married a friend of her brother's, Leonard Woolf. There is a lot of disagreement among scholars about whether the relationship had a positive effect on Virginia's life, but in her letters and writings, she makes it clear that Leonard brought a level of support and stability that she greatly needed. She remained ill for the first three years of their marriage, during which time Leonard nursed her intensively. Later, they moved to Richmond, a district of London further from the centre, so Virginia could enjoy more peace and quiet.

The couple even went into business together. Leonard helped Virginia start a printing press in their home. Although it started as a hobby, the Hogarth Press had some financial success. After a few years, Woolf was publishing and printing most of her books herself. Her sister, Vanessa, illustrated the books and designed the covers.

Woolf had been writing professionally from the age of eighteen, getting articles and reviews published in magazines such as the *Times Literary Supplement*. However, it wasn't until she was 33 that her first novel, *The Voyage Out*, was published. It took her many years to write because of her illness. Her first two books were quite conventional; it wasn't until she saw some of her sister's new paintings that she began to develop a new style of writing which was quite different. Vanessa was painting portraits of people in which the faces were not clearly drawn. Even though the details of the face could not be seen, the paintings still managed to communicate the personality of the people. Virginia transferred this idea to writing, by describing relationships between people, especially men and women, not in the way they talked or behaved to one another, but in what they were thinking and in what they didn't say. This attempt in writing to capture a character's internal thought processes became known as 'stream of consciousness', one of the common features of the modernist style. Along with James Joyce, Virginia Woolf is seen as a literary pioneer of her time. Between 1925 and 1931 she wrote the three books that justify her position as one of the important modernist writers of the 20th century: *Mrs Dalloway*, *To the Lighthouse* and *The Waves*.

The Second World War had a tragic effect on Woolf. She felt that her role as a writer in wartime was useless. Also, the bombing of London put her under a great deal of stress. By March 1941 she was not sleeping or eating, and in her severe depression, she decided to end her own life. She walked into the River Ouse and drowned. Her body was found many days later.

About the story

Lappin and Lapinova was first published in April 1939 in *Harper's Bazaar*, an American women's magazine. In 1944, three years after Virginia's death, Leonard Woolf published a collection of her short stories called *A Haunted House*, and this story was included.

Background information

Hunting and animals in the story

Some of the story uses the metaphor of hunting animals, which was an important activity for various reasons at the time the story was written. People who lived in the countryside often hunted in order to eat. In the United Kingdom, typical animals that were hunted included pheasants, partridges (large birds that spend a lot of time on the ground and are relatively easy to shoot or catch) and rabbits. People would also hunt hares (animals that are similar to rabbits but larger and faster with longer ears and legs) for their meat. One way to hunt is with guns, of course, but rabbits live underground, so one technique that people used to make the rabbits come out of their holes was to send down ferrets, small thin furry animals with long tails that naturally kill and eat rabbits. It was difficult for poor people to hunt wherever they liked because the rich squires who owned most of the land tried to keep the animals living on their land for themselves. People who hunt illegally are called 'poachers'; the landowners employed gamekeepers to stop poachers from hunting on their land.

Hunting for sport, and not for food, was another reason that hunting was popular. Rich people used to ride horses over their land to chase foxes, with the help of fox hounds (dogs that were trained to follow the scent of a fox and lead the hunters to it). The riders would blow on a horn to signal instructions to the hounds. Animals that were caught this way were not eaten. Some hunters liked to show off the animals that they had caught by stuffing them and displaying them in their houses. A special technique called taxidermy used the skins of the animals and preserved them so that they looked as if they were still alive. Foxhunting was made illegal in the United Kingdom in 2004.

Summary

It may help you to know something about what happens in the story before you read it. Don't worry, this summary does not tell you how the story ends!

Rosalind and Ernest are on their honeymoon four days after getting married. In the hotel, Rosalind waits for her husband to come downstairs for breakfast and thinks about her new status as Mrs Ernest Thorburn. When he arrives, she looks at him and decides that there is something about the way his nose moves when he eats that reminds her of her pet rabbit. She tells him what she has noticed. Together, the couple create a shared imaginary rabbit world that they enjoy talking about during the honeymoon.

By the time they return from their holiday, their private world has developed completely. They are often reminded of their rabbit world when they are with friends and family, and the knowledge that they are both thinking about it makes Rosalind feel safe. On one occasion, she is feeling unhappy during a large celebration where Ernest's parents are celebrating fifty years of marriage. But when Ernest moves his nose like a rabbit so that she can see, she is happy again.

The story jumps to two years later, and the couple are living in a nice house, where Rosalind waits for Ernest to come home from the office every day. One evening, she tells him about her day in their private world, but it takes Ernest longer to enter the world with her. It is clear that he is not as enthusiastic about it as he used to be. She has bad dreams and finds that she cannot sleep well. The next day is full of strange emotions and confusion for Rosalind. Something seems to have changed in her life. When Ernest comes home, he finds her sitting, frightened, in the dark. But will he know how to make her feel happy again?

Pre-reading activities

Key vocabulary

This section will help you familiarize yourself with some of the more specific vocabulary used in the story. You may want to use it to help you before you start reading, or as a revision exercise after you have finished the story.

Animals in the story: rabbits

1 **Match the words in bold in the text below with their definitions (a–g).**

Rabbits are very popular animals. Everything about them is cute and seems designed to appeal to children in particular: their little white tails; their **twitching** noses; the way, when they are sitting, that their soft **paws** hang down on their front legs; the way that they sit **bolt upright** on the lookout for danger. Children respond by calling them '**bunny**' and by patting them on the head or holding them in their arms if they are **tame**.

One group of people who definitely do not appreciate rabbits are farmers. Rabbits **nibble** away at crops of vegetables such as lettuces, carrots and cabbages until there is very little left to sell. This wouldn't be a problem if it was just one or two animals, but when food is easy to find, rabbits will quickly **breed** until there is a large population that needs to be controlled.

a) a rabbit. This word is used by children or when talking to children.
b) an animal that is used in contact with people so they are no longer wild
c) if animals do this, they become the parents of young animals; rabbits are known to have lots of young
d) the foot of some animals such as cats, dogs and bears
e) to eat something by taking a lot of small bites
f) to make a sudden short movement
g) with your back very straight

2 **Use the words in bold in exercise 1 in the correct form to complete these sentences (1–7).**

1 San Diego Zoo has announced that two of its pandas have managed to .... successfully.
2 Mel was .... at a chocolate biscuit.
3 Although it was dead, the insect's legs .... slightly for a few more minutes.
4 The teacher read a story to the children about a little .... that had lost his mummy.
5 The rabbit sensed danger and stood .... on its hind legs, watching motionless.
6 The rabbits were so .... that if you approached slowly you could get to within two metres of them.
7 The puppy rolled on to its back with its .... in the air.

Verbs of movement

3 **Look at the definitions of verbs of movement as they are used in the story. Replace the phrases in bold in the sentences (1–12) below with verbs from the box in the correct form.**

---

clutch hold something firmly, for example because you are afraid or in pain, or because you do not want to lose something

dangle hang down or swing without anything stopping you

peer look very carefully, especially because something is difficult to see

ripple if something ripples, it moves gently in small waves

roam move or travel with no particular purpose

saunter walk in a slow and relaxed way

shiver if you shiver, your body shakes slightly, because you are cold or frightened, etc

squat bend your knees and lower yourself towards the ground so that you balance on your feet

start move suddenly because you are afraid or surprised by something

steal off move away quietly and secretly

thrust push something violently or suddenly

wink quickly close and open one eye as a sign to someone

---

1 After he lost his job at the mine, he **travelled** from town to town looking for work.
2 He **wouldn't let go of** the tickets in his hand. The wind was too strong to be careless.
3 The little girl said something that he couldn't hear, so he **crouched down** to listen better.

4   How dare you **walk** in here two hours late? Any more of this attitude and you're fired!

5   I could only just see the road ahead by **looking** through the wet windscreen.

6   My dad never congratulated me or even smiled, but he **signalled with his eye** at me, and that was all I needed to know he was proud.

7   She wasn't expecting him to come in without knocking. The intrusion made her **jump**.

8   Some people go swimming here, even in winter. The thought of it makes me **shake**.

9   The cat was casually **holding** the mouse by its tail in her mouth.

10 The surface of the lake **moved** in the breeze.

11 We didn't have long. Phil **pushed** the money into my hand. 'Be here in an hour,' he said.

12 While Karen wasn't looking, I **walked silently away** to make the phone call.

Types of landscape

4   **The story is set in a variety of landscapes, both real and imaginary. Read the descriptions of the different landscapes. Check any new words in a dictionary. Which types of landscape exist in your country? Do you know of other places that feature these types of landscape?**

A **moor** is a large area of high land covered with grasses and other plants that can live in windy, mountainous conditions. The soil is not good for growing crops, but some plants can grow well, including gorse, a bush with yellow flowers and thorns and heather, a plant with small purple or white flowers. Moors are desolate places, completely empty with no people, trees or other features.

The **prairies** are the large, flat areas in central North America. These are covered with grass and farmland but there are few, if any, trees. Similar open grassland on other continents have different names, such as 'pampas' in South America and 'the steppes' in Eurasia.

A **marsh** is an area of soft, wet land usually close to sea level, or near lakes or large rivers. Trees do not usually grow there. In a **swamp**, which is land that is almost always covered by water, specially adapted trees can grow.

Interiors

Some of the story is set indoors in wealthy middle-class houses in London.

5 **Read the following descriptions. Which paragraph describes a drawing room (an old-fashioned name for a living room) and which describes a bedroom?**

Paragraph 1

The wall was covered in a shiny **satin** wallpaper with a floral design. The **blinds** over the windows were covered in a matching pattern. A full-length **looking glass** stood beside a pretty white **dressing table** which was covered in fine feminine objects: a silver brush and combs, earrings and necklaces and tiny **enamel** boxes containing small **trifles**, such as hairpins and clips.

Paragraph 2

In the centre of the room, above the **mantelpiece** over the fireplace, was a portrait of an important-looking man. A large **mahogany sideboard** dominated the left wall, containing shelves full of silver plates, crystal glasses, antique coins and other **lustrous** possessions. Other dark wood furniture filled the room. On the right wall were **engravings** of family members, including one that looked a lot like the man in the portrait.

6 **Look at the words in bold in paragraphs 1 and 2 in exercise 5 and find the words that match each of the definitions (1–9) below.**

1 a piece of furniture you would find in a woman's bedroom
2 an old-fashioned word for mirror
3 three different materials: a type of fabric, a wood and a hard decorative covering
4 a shelf above a fireplace
5 window covers that you pull down from the top of a window to the bottom
6 an old-fashioned word which refers to small objects of little importance
7 pictures made by cutting a design into metal
8 an adjective that means bright and shiny
9 a large piece of furniture made of wood

7 Complete the description below with the words you found in exercise 6.

We were shown into the drawing room. This is where the family spent time talking, reading and playing games. There was a large (1) .... of Sir Leslie looking down on the room over the (2) .... The furniture was all made of a dark wood – (3) .... perhaps, the largest piece was a huge (4) .... to the right. She then showed us the bedrooms upstairs. In one the (5) .... were drawn so that it was quite dark, but it was clearly a woman's bedroom, with (6) .... pink silk sheets on the bed and shiny (7) .... dresses hanging next to a small (8) ...., on which were carefully placed various lady's (9) .... such as hairbrushes, combs and silver jewellery. An ornate hand-held (10) .... was lying so that the mirror was face down and its pink and purple (11) .... back was showing.

Adjectives describing appearance and personality

8 Read the adjectives and their definitions in the box. Which would you use to:
a) describe appearance?
b) describe personality?

---

bold confident and not afraid of people

coarse rude and offensive

determined not willing to let anything prevent you from doing what you have decided to do

diminutive very short or small

flushed looking red because you are hot or ill, or feel embarrassed or excited

furtive secretive, doing something quickly and secretly to avoid being noticed

plump slightly fat or having a full rounded shape

spruce clean and tidy in appearance

timid shy and nervous

undependable unreliable, an undependable person does not do what they say they will do

wary careful or nervous about possible dangers or problems

Main themes

Before you read the story, you may want to think about some of its main themes. The questions will help you think about the story as you are reading it for the first time. There is more discussion of the main themes in the *Literary analysis* section after the story.

Marriage

The story starts with a wedding and follows the couple through the first years of marriage.

9 As you read the story, think about these questions:

a) In what sense is it a conventional marriage? How is it unusual?
b) What are the strengths of Ernest and Rosalind's relationship? What are the weaknesses?
c) What do Ernest and Rosalind each want from their marriage?

The inner world of the imagination

The story moves between real events, such as Ernest and Rosalind's wedding, to a fantastical world in their minds. They use their fancy, or imagination, to 'play' with this world, building and inhabiting it.

10 As you read, ask yourself:

a) What does their inner world provide Ernest and Rosalind?
b) To what extent do they share the same inner world?
c) Does their private world seem attractive to you? Why? Why not?

Lappin and Lapinova

by Virginia Woolf

They were married. The wedding march[1] **pealed out**. The
pigeons fluttered. Small boys in Eton jackets threw rice; a fox
terrier sauntered across the path; and Ernest Thorburn led his
bride to the car through that small **inquisitive** crowd of complete
strangers which always collects in London to enjoy other people's
happiness or unhappiness. Certainly he looked handsome and
she looked shy. More rice was thrown, and the car moved off.

That was on Tuesday. Now it was Saturday. Rosalind had
still to get used to the fact that she was Mrs Ernest Thorburn.
Perhaps she never would get used to the fact that she was Mrs
Ernest Anybody, she thought, as she sat in the bow window of
the hotel looking over the lake to the mountains, and waited for
her husband to come down to breakfast. Ernest was a difficult
name to get used to. It was not the name she would have chosen.
She would have preferred Timothy, Antony, or Peter. He did
not look like Ernest either. The name suggested the Albert
Memorial[2], mahogany sideboards, steel engravings of the Prince
Consort with his family – her mother-in-law's dining-room in
Porchester Terrace in short.

But here he was. Thank goodness he did not look like Ernest
– no. But what did he look like? She glanced at him sideways.
Well, when he was eating toast he looked like a rabbit. Not
that anyone else would have seen a likeness to a creature so
diminutive and timid in this spruce, muscular young man with
the straight nose, the blue eyes, and the very firm mouth. But

1 the *Wedding March* is a piece of music by composer Mendelssohn often played at the
  end of weddings
2 a monument built in 1872 by Queen Victoria in memory of her husband, the Prince
  Consort

that made it all the more amusing. His nose twitched very slightly when he ate. So did her pet rabbit's. She kept watching his nose twitch; and then she had to explain, when he caught her looking at him, why she laughed.

'It's because you're like a rabbit, Ernest,' she said. 'Like a wild rabbit,' she added, looking at him. 'A hunting rabbit; a King Rabbit; a rabbit that makes laws for all the other rabbits.'

Ernest had no objection to being that kind of rabbit, and since it amused her to see him twitch his nose – he had never known that his nose twitched – he twitched it on purpose. And she laughed and laughed; and he laughed too, so that the maiden[3] ladies and the fishing man and the Swiss waiter in his greasy black jacket all guessed right; they were very happy. But how long does such happiness last? they asked themselves; and each answered according to his own circumstances.

At lunch time, seated on a clump of heather beside the lake, 'Lettuce, rabbit?' said Rosalind, holding out the lettuce that had been provided to eat with the hardboiled eggs. 'Come and take it out of my hand,' she added, and he stretched out and nibbled the lettuce and twitched his nose.

'Good rabbit, nice rabbit,' she said, patting him, as she used to pat her tame rabbit at home. But that was absurd. He was not a tame rabbit, whatever he was. She turned it into French. 'Lapin,' she called him. But whatever he was, he was not a French rabbit. He was simply and solely English-born at Porchester Terrace, educated at Rugby[4]; now a clerk in His Majesty's Civil Service[5]. So she tried 'Bunny' next; but that was worse. 'Bunny' was someone plump and soft and comic; he was thin and hard and serious. Still, his nose twitched. 'Lappin,' she exclaimed suddenly; and gave a little cry as if she had found the very word she looked for.

'Lappin, Lappin, King Lappin,' she repeated. It seemed to suit him exactly; he was not Ernest, he was King Lappin. Why? She did not know.

3 *old-fashioned*: a woman who is not married
4 a famous private school in England
5 Britain's government departments

When there was nothing new to talk about on their long solitary walks – and it rained, as everyone had warned them that it would rain; or when they were sitting over the fire in the evening, for it was cold, and the maiden ladies had gone and the fishing man, and the waiter only came if you rang the bell for him, she let her fancy play with the story of the Lappin tribe. Under her hands – she was sewing; he was reading – they became very real, very **vivid**, very amusing. Ernest put down the paper and helped her. There were the black rabbits and the red; there were the enemy rabbits and the friendly. There were the wood in which they lived and the outlying prairies and the swamp. Above all there was King Lappin, who, far from having only the one trick – that he twitched his nose – became as the days passed an animal of the greatest character; Rosalind was always finding new qualities in him. But above all he was a great hunter.

'And what,' said Rosalind, on the last day of the honeymoon, 'did the King do to-day?'

In fact they had been climbing all day; and she had worn a **blister** on her heel; but she did not mean that.

'To-day,' said Ernest, twitching his nose as he bit the end off his cigar, 'he chased a hare.' He paused; struck a match, and twitched again.

'A woman hare,' he added.

'A white hare!' Rosalind exclaimed, as if she had been expecting this. 'Rather a small hare; silver grey; with big bright eyes?'

'Yes,' said Ernest, looking at her as she had looked at him, 'a smallish animal; with eyes popping out of her head, and two little front paws dangling.' It was exactly how she sat, with her sewing dangling in her hands; and her eyes, that were so big and bright, were certainly a little prominent.

'Ah, Lapinova,' Rosalind murmured.

'Is that what she's called?' said Ernest – 'the real Rosalind?' He looked at her. He felt very much in love with her.

'Yes; that's what she's called,' said Rosalind. 'Lapinova.' And before they went to bed that night it was all **settled**. He was King Lappin; she was Queen Lapinova. They were the opposite of each other; he was bold and determined; she wary and undependable. He ruled over the busy world of rabbits; her world was a desolate, mysterious place, which she ranged mostly by moonlight. All the same, their territories touched; they were King and Queen.

Thus when they came back from their honeymoon they possessed a private world, inhabited, save[6] for the one white hare, entirely by rabbits. No one guessed that there was such a place, and that of course made it all the more amusing. It made them feel, more even than most young married couples, **in league** together against the rest of the world. Often they looked **slyly** at each other when people talked about rabbits and woods and traps and shooting. Or they winked furtively across the table when Aunt Mary said that she could never bear to see a hare in a dish – it looked so like a baby: or when John, Ernest's sporting brother, told them what price rabbits were fetching that autumn in Wiltshire, skins and all. Sometimes when they wanted a gamekeeper, or a poacher or a Lord of the Manor, they amused themselves by distributing the parts among their friends. Ernest's mother, Mrs Reginald Thorburn, for example, fitted the part of the Squire to perfection. But it was all secret – that was the point of it; nobody save themselves knew that such a world existed.

Without that world, how, Rosalind wondered, that winter could she have lived at all? For instance, there was the golden-wedding party, when all the Thorburns assembled at Porchester Terrace to celebrate the fiftieth anniversary of that union which had been so **blessed** – had it not produced Ernest Thorburn? and so fruitful – had it not produced nine other sons and daughters into the bargain, many themselves married and also fruitful? She **dreaded** that party. But it was inevitable. As she walked upstairs she felt bitterly that she was an only child and an orphan at that; a **mere** drop among all those Thorburns assembled in the great drawing-room with the shiny satin wallpaper and the lustrous

6 *formal*: except

family portraits. The living Thorburns much resembled the painted; save that instead of painted lips they had real lips; out of which came jokes; jokes about schoolrooms, and how they had pulled the chair from under the governess[7]; jokes about frogs and how they had put them between the virgin sheets of maiden ladies. As for herself, she had never even made an apple-pie bed[8]. Holding her present in her hand she advanced toward her mother-in-law **sumptuous** in yellow satin; and toward her father-in-law decorated with a rich yellow **carnation**. All round them on tables and chairs there were golden tributes, some nestling in cotton wool; others branching **resplendent** – candlesticks; cigar boxes; chains; each stamped with the goldsmith's proof that it was solid gold, hall-marked, authentic. But her present was only a little pinchbeck[9] box pierced with holes; an old sand caster, an eighteenth-century relic, once used to sprinkle sand over wet ink. Rather a senseless present she felt – in an age of blotting paper[10]; and as she proffered it, she saw in front of her the **stubby** black handwriting in which her mother-in-law when they were engaged had expressed the hope that 'My son will make you happy.' No, she was not happy. Not at all happy. She looked at Ernest, straight as a **ramrod** with a nose like all the noses in the family portraits; a nose that never twitched at all.

Then they went down to dinner. She was half hidden by the great chrysanthemums that curled their red and gold petals into large tight balls. Everything was gold. A gold-edged card with gold initials **intertwined** recited the list of all the dishes that would be set one after another before them. She dipped her spoon in a plate of clear golden fluid. The raw white fog outside had been turned by the lamps into a golden mesh that **blurred** the edges of the plates and gave the pineapples a rough golden

---

7 *old-fashioned*: a woman whose job was to teach her employer's children in their home
8 a practical joke in which the victim cannot get into bed because the sheet is folded in a special way
9 a metal alloy of zinc and copper that looks like gold
10 special paper that you use for drying the ink when you have just finished writing with a fountain pen

skin. Only she herself in her white wedding dress peering ahead of her with her prominent eyes seemed insoluble as an **icicle**.

As the dinner wore on, however, the room grew steamy with heat. Beads of perspiration stood out on the men's foreheads. She felt that her icicle was being turned to water. She was being melted; **dispersed**; dissolved into nothingness; and would soon **faint**. Then through the surge in her head and the **din** in her ears she heard a woman's voice exclaim, 'But they breed so!'

The Thorburns – yes; they breed so, she echoed; looking at all the round red faces that seemed doubled in the **giddiness** that overcame her; and magnified in the gold mist that enhaloed[11] them. 'They breed so.' Then John **bawled**:

'Little devils! … Shoot 'em! Jump on 'em with big boots! That's the only way to deal with 'em … rabbits!'

At that word, that magic word, she revived. Peeping between the chrysanthemums she saw Ernest's nose twitch. It rippled, it ran with successive twitches. And at that a mysterious catastrophe befell the Thorburns. The golden table became a moor with the gorse in full bloom; the din of voices turned to one peal of **lark**'s laughter ringing down from the sky. It was a blue sky – clouds passed slowly. And they had all been changed – the Thorburns. She looked at her father-in-law, a furtive little man with dyed moustaches. His **foible** was collecting things – seals, enamel boxes, trifles from eighteenth-century dressing tables which he hid in the drawers of his study from his wife. Now she saw him as he was – a poacher, stealing off with his coat bulging with pheasants and partridges to drop them **stealthily** into a three-legged pot in his smoky little cottage. That was her real father-in-law – a poacher. And Celia, the unmarried daughter, who always nosed out other people's secrets, the little things they wished to hide – she was a white ferret with pink eyes, and a nose clotted with earth from her horrid underground nosings and pokings. Slung round men's shoulders, in a net[12], and thrust down a hole – it was a **pitiable** life – Celia's; it was none of her

11 *uncommon*: if something is enhaloed, it is surrounded with a halo, a circle of light, around an object
12 ferrets were carried in nets hung from the shoulder

fault. So she saw Celia. And then she looked at her mother-in-law – whom they dubbed The Squire. Flushed, coarse, a bully – she was all that, as she stood returning thanks, but now that Rosalind – that is Lapinova – saw her, she saw behind her the **decayed** family mansion, the plaster peeling off the walls, and heard her, with a **sob** in her voice, giving thanks to her children (who hated her) for a world that had ceased to exist. There was a sudden silence. They all stood with their glasses raised; they all drank; then it was over.

'Oh, King Lappin!' she cried as they went home together in the fog, 'if your nose hadn't twitched just at that moment, I should have been trapped!'

'But you're safe,' said King Lappin, pressing her paw.

'Quite safe,' she answered.

And they drove back through the Park, King and Queen of the marsh, of the mist, and of the gorse-scented moor.

Thus time passed; one year; two years of time. And on a winter's night, which happened by a coincidence to be the anniversary of the golden-wedding party – but Mrs Reginald Thorburn was dead; the house was **to let**; and there was only a caretaker in residence – Ernest came home from the office. They had a nice little home; half a house above a saddler's shop[13] in South Kensington, not far from the tube[14] station. It was cold, with fog in the air, and Rosalind was sitting over the fire, sewing.

'What d'you think happened to me to-day?' she began as soon as he had settled himself down with his legs stretched to the blaze. 'I was crossing the stream when –'

'What stream?' Ernest interrupted her.

'The stream at the bottom, where our wood meets the black wood,' she explained.

Ernest looked completely blank for a moment.

'What the deuce[15] are you talking about?' he asked.

---

13 *old fashioned, British*: a shop where saddles for horses and other leather products are sold

14 the London Underground, a public transport system within the city of London

15 *old-fashioned*: used in questions for emphasizing how surprised or annoyed you are

'My dear Ernest!' she cried in dismay. 'King Lappin,' she added, dangling her little front paws in the firelight. But his nose did not twitch. Her hands – they turned to hands – clutched the stuff she was holding; her eyes popped half out of her head. It took him five minutes at least to change from Ernest Thorburn to King Lappin; and while she waited she felt a load on the back of her neck, as if somebody were about to wring it. At last he changed to King Lappin; his nose twitched; and they spent the evening roaming the woods much as usual.

But she slept badly. In the middle of the night she woke, feeling as if something strange had happened to her. She was **stiff** and cold. At last she turned on the light and looked at Ernest lying beside her. He was sound asleep. He snored. But even though he snored, his nose remained perfectly still. It looked as if it had never twitched at all. Was it possible that he was really Ernest; and that she was really married to Ernest? A vision of her mother-in-law's dining-room came before her; and there they sat, she and Ernest, grown old, under the engravings, in front of the sideboard. ... It was their golden-wedding day. She could not bear it.

'Lappin, King Lappin!' she whispered, and for a moment his nose seemed to twitch **of its own accord**. But he still slept. 'Wake up, Lappin, wake up!' she cried.

Ernest woke; and seeing her sitting bolt upright beside him he asked:

'What's the matter?'

'I thought my rabbit was dead!' she **whimpered**. Ernest was angry.

'Don't talk such rubbish, Rosalind,' he said. 'Lie down and go to sleep.'

He turned over. In another moment he was sound asleep and snoring.

But she could not sleep. She lay curled up on her side of the bed, like a hare in its form. She had turned out the light, but the street lamp lit the ceiling faintly, and the trees outside made a **lacy** network over it as if there were a shadowy grove on the ceiling in which she wandered, turning, twisting, in and out, round and round, hunting, being hunted, hearing the bay of hounds and horns; flying, escaping ... until the maid drew the blinds and brought their early tea.

Next day she could settle to nothing. She seemed to have lost something. She felt as if her body had shrunk; it had grown small, and black and hard. Her joints seemed stiff too, and when she looked in the glass, which she did several times as she wandered about the flat, her eyes seemed to burst out of her head, like currants in a bun[16]. The rooms also seemed to have shrunk. Large pieces of furniture jutted out at odd angles and she found herself knocking against them. At last she put on her hat and went out. She walked along the Cromwell Road; and every room she passed and peered into seemed to be a dining-room where people sat eating under steel engravings, with thick yellow lace curtains, and mahogany sideboards. At last she reached the Natural History Museum; she used to like it when she was a child. But the first thing she saw when she went in was a stuffed hare standing on **sham** snow with pink glass eyes. Somehow it made her shiver all over. Perhaps it would be better when **dusk** fell. She went home and sat over the fire, without a light, and tried to imagine that she was out alone on a moor; and there was a stream rushing; and beyond the stream a dark wood. But she could get no further than the stream. At last she squatted down on the bank on the wet grass, and sat crouched in her chair, with her hands dangling empty, and her eyes glazed, like glass eyes, in the firelight. Then there was the crack of a gun.... She started as if she had been shot. It was only Ernest, turning his key in the door. She waited, trembling. He came in and switched on the light. There he stood, tall, handsome, rubbing his hands that were red with cold.

'Sitting in the dark?' he said.

'Oh, Ernest, Ernest!' she cried, starting up in her chair.

'Well, what's up now?' he asked briskly, warming his hands at the fire.

16 a currant bun is a small cake filled with dark dried fruit

'It's Lapinova …' she faltered, glancing wildly at him out of her great startled eyes. 'She's gone, Ernest. I've lost her!'

Ernest frowned. He pressed his lips tight together. 'Oh, that's what's up, is it?' he said, smiling rather **grimly** at his wife. For ten seconds he stood there, silent; and she waited, feeling hands tightening at the back of her neck.

'Yes,' he said at length. 'Poor Lapinova …' He straightened his tie at the looking-glass over the mantelpiece.

'Caught in a trap,' he said, 'killed,' and sat down and read the newspaper.

So that was the end of that marriage.

Post-reading activities

Understanding the story

Use these questions to help you check that you have understood the story.

The wedding day and after

1 At what point in Ernest and Roslind's wedding does the story begin?
2 Why are they in a hotel?
3 What does she dislike about her husband? Why?
4 To what extent does Ernest look like a rabbit? What is it about him that reminds her of one?
5 Who are 'the maiden ladies and the fishing man'?
6 How does Ernest encourage the creation of their imaginary world?
7 How is Rosalind similar to her character, the hare?
8 What is their attitude to other people now that they are married?
9 What sort of things remind them of their private world?
10 Why does Rosalind feel uncomfortable at the golden-wedding party?
11 At what moment does the party improve for Rosalind? What happens?
12 What does she imagine the following people to be in her fantasy: Mr Thorburn? Celia? Mrs Thorburn?

Two years later

13 What has Ernest spent the day doing? What about Rosalind?
14 Why is that evening different from normal?
15 What is she so afraid of that she can't sleep?
16 What does she do the following day?
17 What happens at the end of the story? Why?

Language study

Grammar

Ellipsis

Ellipsis is a common feature of spoken English. Normally, a sentence contains a subject and a verb:

> **Ernest was** *a difficult name to get used to.* **It was** *not the name she would have chosen.*

But in speech, words are often omitted at the beginning of a sentence if the meaning is still clear. Notice how in the second sentence that Rosalind says below, she leaves out a subject and a verb (*You're*). This is an example of ellipsis:

'It's because you're like a rabbit, Ernest,' she said. 'Like a wild rabbit'

1 What single word is omitted in the sentence below?

They were the opposite of each other; he was bold and determined; she wary and undependable.

2 Ellipsis can also be used in questions. Look at the example below. What words have been omitted here?

'Sitting in the dark?' he said.

Ellipsis is not restricted to speech. It can be used to avoid repetition and for style in stories, and may lend the writing a literary style. The writer uses a form of ellipsis in the story that is unusual in everyday English; she omits a repeated noun, leaving the adjective that describes it:

There were the black rabbits and the red; there were the enemy rabbits and the friendly.

This type of ellipsis sounds literary and would not be appropriate in everyday English. You would normally avoid a repetition of *rabbits* by replacing it with the pronoun *ones*: *the red ones … the friendly ones.*

Another form of ellipsis, where the writer uses incomplete sentences, is used in the story to create different effects.

3 Look at the two extracts below. What words have been omitted in the phrases in bold?

1) *All round them on tables and chairs there were golden tributes, **some nestling** in cotton wool; **others branching** resplendent – candlesticks; cigar boxes; chains; **each stamped** with the goldsmith's proof that it was solid gold, hall-marked, authentic.*

2) *But her present was only a little pinchbeck box **pierced with holes**; an old sand caster, an eighteenth-century relic, **once used** to sprinkle sand over wet ink. **Rather a senseless present** she felt – in an age of blotting paper …*

4 Look again at the two extracts in exercise 3. Match the effect ellipsis has in each extract with a) or b) below.

a) It follows Rosalind's thought processes.

b) It emphasizes the quantity of gold things in the room.

5 Look at the following extracts. Cross out any words that can be omitted. Then check your answers with the original story.

1 *The name suggested the Albert Memorial, mahogany sideboards, steel engravings of the Prince Consort with his family – The name suggested her mother-in-law's dining-room in Porchester Terrace in short.* (page 111)

2 *He paused; he struck a match, and he twitched again.* (page 113)

3 *The living Thorburns much resembled the painted Thorburns.* (page 115)

4 *Holding her present in her hand she advanced toward her mother-in-law sumptuous in yellow satin; and she advanced toward her father-in-law decorated with a rich yellow carnation.* (page 115)

5 *No, she was not happy. She was not at all happy.* (page 115)

6 *'But you're safe,' said King Lappin, pressing her paw.* (page 117)
   'I'm quite safe,' she answered.

7 *They had a nice little home; it was half a house above a saddler's shop in South Kensington, and it was not far from the tube station.* (page 117)

8 *She ... tried to imagine that she was out alone on a moor; and there was a stream rushing; and beyond the stream there was a dark wood.* (page 119)

9 *'Poor Lapinova ... She was caught in a trap,' he said, 'She was killed,' and he sat down and he read the newspaper.* (page 120)

Vocabulary

Discourse markers

There is relatively little dialogue in the story. We learn about the characters mostly by reading Rosalind's thoughts and opinions about the people and events. These thoughts jump from one idea to the next, and are linked and related to each other using discourse markers.

6 Match the discourse markers in bold with their uses and synonyms (a–h).

1 *But what did he look like? ...* **Well**, *when he was eating toast he looked like a rabbit.*

2 *The name suggested the Albert Memorial, mahogany sideboards, steel engravings of the Prince Consort with his family – her mother-in-law's dining-room in Porchester Terrace* **in short**.

3 *There were the black rabbits and the red; there were the enemy rabbits and the friendly. There were the wood in which they lived and the outlying prairies and the swamp.* **Above all** *there was King Lappin ...*

4 *They were the opposite of each other; he was bold and determined; she wary and undependable.* **All the same,** *their territories touched; they were King and Queen.*

5 *Their territories touched; they were King and Queen.* **Thus** *when they came back from their honeymoon they possessed a private world ...*

6 *... when he was eating toast he looked like a rabbit.* **Not that** *anyone else would have seen a likeness to a creature so diminutive ...*

7 *Without that world, how, Rosalind wondered, that winter could she have lived at all?* **For instance**, *there was the golden-wedding party...*

8 *... jokes about frogs and how they had put them between the virgin sheets of maiden ladies.* **As for** *herself, she had never even made an apple-pie bed.*

a) (formal) explaining the result of a fact that you have just mentioned (*so ...*)

b) introducing a fact or statement that contradicts what has just been mentioned (*even so ...*)

c) adding a negative statement that reduces the effect or the importance of what you have just said (*that doesn't mean ...*)

d) introducing a statement, especially one that you make as a reply (*Let me think ...*)

e) introducing a subject that is related to what you have just been talking about (*regarding ...*)

f) signalling a summary of something that you have just said (*in other words ...*)

g) introducing an example (*for example, ...*)
h) referring to something that is more important than any of the other things you could mention (*most importantly ...*)

7 Match sentences 1–8 with sentences that follow (a–h). Use a discourse marker from the extracts in exercise 6 to join them.

1 Fewer pupils will attend the schools.
2 We will all surely miss Jack, and for different reasons.
3 I'm sure he's safe.
4 Inflation is up, spending is down.
5 The parents enjoyed the relaxation.
6 We forgot to leave our number.
7 What would you recommend for toothache?
8 You may have questions which you wish to raise.

a) ...., he'll be remembered as a loving husband and family man.
b) .... the children, they were happy enough to spend all day on the beach.
c) But ...., I wish he'd come home.
d) ...., who will oversee your work and how will feedback be given?
e) ...., the economy is in poor shape.
f) .... it matters; they can always ask Julie.
g) They will .... need fewer teachers.
h) ...., you could try gargling salt water.

Literary analysis

Plot

1 List the most significant events of the plot. How important are they to the story? Where does the most significant action take place?
2 How are real events affected by the inner world of the characters? How is the inner world affected by real events?
3 Are there any events that take place purely in the world of the rabbits?
4 It states that during the party Rosalind was 'not happy. Not at all happy' with Ernest. In the same passage it says that his nose 'never twitched at all'. Yet we know that his nose did twitch, certainly at this early stage in their marriage. Do you think her unhappiness is a permanent state at this point or merely an expression of how she is feeling at the party?

5   Do you think that 'the end of that marriage' means one of them
    leaving and divorce, or do they continue to live together as husband
    and wife in some way?
6   Who do you think is most to blame for the unhappy ending?
7   What could Rosalind have done to save her marriage? Do you think
    she would have been able to do this?
8   What does the story say about marriage?

Character

9   Look at the first paragraph. What adjectives are used to describe
    Rosalind and Ernest? Whose external appearance is described and
    whose personality is described? What does this suggest?
10 What do we know about Ernest's personality? What adjective would
    you use to describe him at the start of the story? Can you think of
    more adjectives to describe him towards the end of the story?
11 What are the similarities between Rosalind and Lapinova in terms
    of both appearance and personality?
12 How does the following extract reflect the different concerns of
    Ernest and Rosalind?

    *They were the opposite of each other; he was bold and determined; she
    wary and undependable. He ruled over the busy world of rabbits; her
    world was a desolate, mysterious place, which she ranged mostly by
    moonlight. All the same, their territories touched; they were King and
    Queen.*

13 How are the rest of the Thorburns described in the story? Why
    is this? What do they represent to Rosalind? Do we see the real
    Thorburns objectively?
14 Why does Ernest say at the end: 'Poor Lapinova … Caught in a
    trap, killed'? Do you think he is being deliberately cruel or is there
    another interpretation for his comment?
15 Do you sympathize with Rosalind (do you like her, care about her,
    or feel her emotions)? Why? Why not?

Animals in the story

16 Describe the animals in the story.
17 Why does Rosalind describe King Lappin to Ernest as 'wild',
    'hunting', a 'King rabbit'?
18 What do the animals mean for their relationship from Rosalind's
    point of view? What about from Ernest's point of view?

Narration

19 Read the first paragraph again (page 111). How much of their wedding do we read about? What is the effect of this?

20 Whose point of view is the sentence in the first paragraph: 'Certainly he looked handsome and she looked shy'? Whose point of view is the rest of the story, starting in the following paragraph?

21 What impression of the story teller do you get from the phrase in the first paragraph: 'other people's happiness or unhappiness'?

22 What do the following extracts tell us about the development of Ernest and Rosalind's relationship as the story progresses?

On honeymoon

'And what,' said Rosalind, on the last day of the honeymoon, 'did the King do to-day?'

  In fact they had been climbing all day; and she had worn a blister on her heel; but she did not mean that.

  'To-day,' said Ernest, twitching his nose as he bit the end off his cigar, 'he chased a hare.' He paused; struck a match, and twitched again.

Two years later

'What d'you think happened to me to-day?' she began as soon as he had settled himself down with his legs stretched to the blaze. 'I was crossing the stream when –'

  'What stream?' Ernest interrupted her.

  'The stream at the bottom, where our wood meets the black wood,' she explained.

  Ernest looked completely blank for a moment.

  'What the deuce are you talking about?' he asked.

23 How does Rosalind's interpretation of events affect the telling of the story? How would the story have been different if it had been told from Ernest's point of view?

Style

24 Read the first paragraph again (page 111). Notice how short the sentences are. What effect does this have on the account of the wedding? Notice, too, the use of the passive voice: 'More rice was thrown'. What effect does this have?

25 Read the long paragraph on page 119 that starts: 'Next day she could settle to nothing ...' Here, too, the sentences are mostly quite short, but the effect is quite different. How does the style of the paragraph reflect Rosalind's state of mind?

26 Read again the long paragraph on page 116 that starts: 'At that word, that magic word …' Notice the way that ideas and words are repeated and sentences broken and interrupted by other phrases: '*At that word, that magic word…*'; '*…she saw Ernest's nose twitch. It rippled, it ran with successive twitches…*'; '*… laughter ringing down from the sky. It was a blue sky*'. Read the rest of the paragraph and find more repeated words and examples of fragmented sentences. What is the effect of this style?

27 In the long paragraph on page 119, it says that although she is at home, she 'tried to imagine that she was out alone on a moor'. How does the following sentence reflect her difficulty?

   At last she squatted down on the bank on the wet grass, and sat crouched in her chair, with her hands dangling empty, and her eyes glazed, like glass eyes, in the firelight.

28 What do you think of the final sentence? Is it too short, do you think? What do you think the writer meant by stopping the story so suddenly?

Guidance to the above literary terms, answer keys to all the exercises and activities, plus a wealth of other reading-practice material, can be found at: www.macmillanenglish.com/readers.

Brown Wolf
by Jack London

About the author

John Griffith London was born in San Francisco in 1876. His mother, Flora Wellman, was a music teacher from a wealthy background. She was not married to the man who was probably Jack's father – the journalist, lawyer and astrologer, William Chaney – so the young writer took the name of his stepfather, John London. In his teens, the young John London became known as Jack.

Flora and John were poor and Jack's childhood was hard. He had little formal education, and started work when he was very young to bring in extra money – by the time he was a teenager, Jack was working 16 hours a day at a local factory. For several years the young writer went from job to job and place to place taking any work he could, including deep sea fishing, shovelling coal, doing manual work in factories, even stealing oysters in Oakland Bay. In between, he travelled. His journey on a freight (cargo) train across America provided much of the material for his partly autobiographical book, *The Road* (1907).

Returning to San Francisco when his stepfather died, Jack took a job in a laundry to earn enough money to support his mother. Still writing, but as yet unpublished, he studied at the same time, gaining a place at the University of Berkeley in California, though he did not complete his degree. At the age of 25 his first short story was published. It was an immediate success, and after years of hard work and poverty, London went on to become one of the highest paid and most celebrated writers of his generation.

Some of London's most loved stories and novels concern animals, especially dogs. He had grown up with a pet dog called Rollo; perhaps this was where his love of dogs came from. The relationship between dogs and their human owners is a theme he often returns to in his writing. The way that human actions affected dogs' behaviour was of particular interest to him. For example, an early story called *Diable – A Dog*, published in 1902, tells of how a dog kills its owner after being treated cruelly by him. He returns to this theme again in one of his most famous novels, *The Call of the Wild* (1903), in which a domestic dog is stolen from his home in California and sent to the north of Canada to live a harsh life as a sled dog pulling sleds for men. In 1906, London wrote a similar novel, *White Fang*, except that this time the main character is a wolfdog, a mixture of the two species. Both these novels examine in great detail the power of nature and instinct over dogs' more domestic relationship with people. The dog in *The Call of the Wild* has to learn to be aggressive in order to survive in the wild, while White Fang's journey takes him in the opposite direction, from Canada to California and from the harsh existence in the wild to a life as a domestic dog.

By the time he was 30, London had already lived a full life. He had been married, had two children and got divorced. He married again to Charmian Kittredge, with whom he travelled widely. As famous for his adventures as his writing, London was charismatic and good-looking, telling stories based on his experiences. In addition to his writing novels and short stories, he also worked as a war correspondent, rode horses in his ranch in California, hosted extravagant parties, was an enthusiastic amateur boxer and sailed across the South Pacific with Charmian.

London's work ethic continued throughout his life, and his commitment to writing 1000 words per day meant that he produced a great deal of work – his main subjects and themes were often adventure and difficulty. He continued to work hard and play hard until his death in 1916 at the age of 40, from kidney failure related to his heavy drinking. He left more than 50 fiction and nonfiction books, hundreds of short stories and numerous articles.

Details about the life and character of Jack London are controversial, but what is certain is that he took advantage of what life had to offer, travelling and having adventures, and writing about what he called 'big moments of living'.

About the story

Brown Wolf was published in *Everybody's Magazine* in August 1906. It was later released in a collection, *Brown Wolf and Other Jack London Stories*, about life in the west of the United States and Canada.

'Wolf' was clearly a favourite word of London's. To his close friends, he was known as Wolf, and even signed letters using that name. He spent a large part of his fortune on a huge mansion, which he named 'Wolf House'.

Background information

The Klondike Gold Rush

Wherever gold is found, it creates a lot of excitement. Throughout the 19th century, the countries of Australia, Brazil, Canada, South Africa and the United States experienced 'gold rushes', periods when many people went to areas where gold had been discovered in order to become rich. The existence of gold was a chance for ordinary people to make a lot of money very quickly. However, many people ended up poorer than before.

Gold was discovered in Canada, in a region called the Yukon, along the Klondike river, in 1896. This became known as the last 'great gold rush', and during the three years that it lasted, over 100 000 men made their way north in search of gold. The journey through snowy mountains and terrible conditions was so difficult that just a third of them arrived. Of these, only about 4000 people struck gold.

Jack London travelled to the Yukon in 1897, aged 21, and tried prospecting (searching for a mineral like gold) but returned less than a year later. Although he never struck gold, he listened to the stories of the difficult lives people led there. Later, he turned some of these into the novels that helped him make his fortune.

Sled dogs

In winter in the days of the gold rush, the only quick way to travel long distances through the snow was by sled, where a team of dogs would pull a vehicle with long pieces of wood fitted to the bottom. Some gold camps were impossible to reach without a dog sled. The person who drove the sled was known as the 'musher' because of the shout he would use to make the dogs run: 'Mush!'

Summary

It may help you to know something about what happens in the story before you read it. Don't worry, this summary does not tell you how the story ends!

Walt and Madge Irvine live in a beautiful area of the countryside in California. Walt makes money as a poet, selling poems to magazines. One day a wild-looking dog arrives at their cottage, very hungry and in poor condition. They offer him food, which he eats but he refuses to let them come close or touch him. They call him 'Wolf' because he looks like one. He stays near their house for a few days, but once he recovers and his strength returns, he disappears.

The couple don't think that they will ever see Wolf again. Later, however, Walt is travelling to the north of California by train when he looks out of the window and sees Wolf running along the railway track. They are 200 miles away from where he started. Walt decides to get off at the next stop. He uses a piece of meat to capture Wolf and take him back home. He puts a collar on him that has Walt's name and address on it.

But as soon as they release Wolf, he runs away again. The next day a telegram arrives from a place one hundred miles to the north telling Walt to come and pick up his dog.

They tie him up for a few days, but again, as soon as they let him go, he escapes. This keeps happening, until after a year Wolf gives up trying and settles down with the Irvines. It still takes them many months before he will let them touch him, but finally he accepts their affection. Mrs Johnson, a neighbour of the Irvines, has a brother who lives in the Klondike and she believes that this is where Wolf is from, which would explain why he always wanted to go north when he escapes.

The couple are out walking in the countryside on their way to the post office, when a large man approaches in the opposite direction. Wolf is somewhere nearby in the forest. The man asks for directions to his sister, Mrs Johnson's house, and Madge guesses correctly that he must be her brother from the Klondike. His name is Skiff Miller.

Just then, Wolf appears from the bushes. Skiff notices him and is immediately interested in the dog. For the first time since the Irvines have known Wolf, he walks up to this stranger without growling or showing his teeth. Instead, he licks his hand and lets Skiff pet him. Why is Wolf being so friendly? Does Wolf know this man? Could he hold the secret of Wolf's mysterious past?

Pre-reading activities

Key vocabulary

This section will help you familiarize yourself with some of the more specific vocabulary used in the story. You may want to use it to help you before you start reading, or as a revision exercise after you have finished the story.

Animals in the story: verbs describing a dog's actions

We learn a lot about how the dog in the story is feeling and thinking by the way it moves its body and behaves.

1 **Read the definitions and try to imagine a dog doing these things. Which actions:**
   a) **make a noise?**
   b) **may show anger?**
   c) **may show excitement?**

---

bare its fangs show its teeth
bark make a short loud sound
bristle if an animal's fur bristles, it sticks up because it is angry or afraid
crawl move along with your body close to the ground
growl make a frightening low noise in the throat
howl make a long loud sound. Wolves often make this sound.
pant breathe loudly with your mouth open, for example, when you have been running
snarl make a short sound in the throat and show the teeth
sniff breathe in noisily through the nose, for example, to smell something
squirm move by twisting and turning in a small space
whine if a dog whines, it makes a long high noise, usually because it wants something

---

2 **Choose the correct form of the verbs from exercise 1 to complete the following sentences.**
   1 He walked slowly with his nose close to the ground, *crawling / sniffing* for signs of the missing boy.
   2 I wish the neighbours would stop their dog from *barking / bristling* all night. I can't sleep!
   3 It *barked / crawled* under a small space at the bottom of the fence and escaped.

4 It was obvious that their dog didn't like me. It wouldn't stop *growling / panting* at me the whole time I was there.

5 The dog lay *howling / panting* for about ten minutes when it came back from its walk. It was too tired to even drink any water.

6 The dog wouldn't stop *bearing its teeth / whining* until it was given food from the table.

7 The first sign that he doesn't like another dog is when you can see his hairs *bristling / squirming* on his back.

8 Typical sounds in movies that create a feeling of horror are the wind in the trees or an animal *baring its fangs / howling* in the distance.

9 When I returned, Coco was so excited she *snarled / squirmed* around my legs, licking my hands for several minutes.

10 It tells me very clearly that it doesn't want me near it. Every time I try to come close it *snarls / whines*.

The countryside

The main characters in the story live in a cottage in the countryside and the land around their house is described in detail.

3 **Read the following passage. Match the words in bold to their definitions (a–n).**

He woke early and continued on his journey. It hadn't rained but the ground was wet with morning **dew**. Thirsty, he found a **spring** from which a clear **brook** ran, over rocks all grown over with **moss**. He followed the **trail** he had started on the previous day. Spring was coming and the trees were displaying small pink and white **buds**, though the **blossom** wasn't out yet.

At midday he found an old **log** to sit on to eat the bread and cheese that was left. While he ate he threw **pebbles** at a nearby tree. Rested, he carried on. The trail had disappeared and now he was navigating from memory. Sometimes it was easy to move, with bare earth or perhaps a **fern-brake** to walk over; other times he had to push through dense **thickets** of vegetation where little light could get through.

Suddenly he found himself in an **orchard**. He recognized the peach trees that he had planted with his father years before. He walked faster in the direction he knew to be right. There was the small **grove** of trees that he had hidden in as a boy. And there was the cottage of his childhood, at the side of the **clearing**, looking just as it had all that time ago.

a) the flowers on a tree or bush
b) a group of plants with leaves shaped like feathers and no flowers
c) a small wood or group of trees
d) a path through the countryside
e) a small river
f) a small stone, especially one that has been made smooth by water
g) a soft green plant that grows in a layer on wet rocks or trees
h) a thick piece of wood cut from a tree
i) tightly curled up parts of a plant that open to form leaves or flowers
j) an area in a forest where there are no trees or bushes
k) an area of land where fruit trees are grown
l) an area with a lot of bushes and small trees growing very close together
m) small drops of water that form on the ground during the night
n) water that flows up from under the ground and forms a small pool

Hardship and comfort

The story takes place in the comfort and relative ease of the Irvine's cottage in sunny California. This is contrasted with living conditions in northern Canada, which is a much colder and harsher place to survive.

4 Read the definitions in the box below. Which words are associated with: a) an easy life? b) a hard life?

---

a soft berth (n) a berth is a bed (often on a train or ship)

caress (v) move your hands gently over someone's face or body in a way that shows you love them

demonstrative (adj) showing kindness or love in the way that you behave towards someone

famine (n) a serious lack of food that continues for a long time and causes many people in a country to become ill or die

footsore (adj) *literary:* with feet that hurt because of walking a lot

frost (n) a thin white layer of ice that looks like powder and forms on things outside when the weather is very cold

lean (adj) thin with very little fat on you

ordeal (n) an extremely unpleasant experience, especially one that lasts for a long time

recuperate (v) get better after being ill or injured

savage (adj) a savage animal is likely to attack you

snuggle (v) put yourself into a warm, comfortable position, for example by sitting with your body against someone else's body

toil (n) difficult and tiring work, especially physical work

whip-lash (n) a hit from a whip, a long thin piece of leather used for making horses or other animals move faster

wretched (adj) in very bad condition, unhappy or ill

Formal verbs

London's style is characterised by a wide range of formal vocabulary. The effect of this is discussed in the *Literary analysis* section after the story. In the box below are some formal verbs that are found in the story.

5 Read the definitions, then choose one verb in the correct form to replace the words and phrases in the sentences (1–10).

---

articulate express thoughts and ideas clearly and effectively

aver to say something in a very determined way because you believe strongly in it or you are certain it is true

constitute if something constitutes something else, it is the same as that something

discourse talk for a long time about a particular subject

enunciate pronounce words clearly so that they can be easily understood

expend use time, energy, money, etc, doing something

possess if you are possessed by an emotion, you feel that emotion very strongly

proceed go in a particular direction

proclaim state something publicly

traverse move over or across an area

---

1 He **announced** his innocence from the top of the courtroom steps.
2 He was **gripped** by a desire to visit his grandfather's house where he had spent so many childhood holidays.
3 Her accent was recognizably Arabic but she **pronounced** each word beautifully and clearly.
4 He's under a great deal of emotional stress. This makes it difficult for him to **say** what he really feels.
5 I was **driving** towards the scene of the crime when I noticed a man running in the opposite direction.
6 It wasn't until the 1950s that most geologists **claimed with confidence** that the continents are, in fact, moving.
7 Ernest Shackleton's daring plan was to **cross** the entire continent of Antarctica.
8 The two women sat **talking at length** about crime and poverty.
9 They **spent** an inordinate amount of energy trying to control their children.
10 This letter does not **represent** an offer of employment.

Phrasal verbs

6 Match the verbs in bold in the sentences (1–10) below to their definitions (a–j).

1 You'd better be **getting along** now. It's already late.
2 'Hilary,' he **broke in** gently, 'I'm just trying to help.'
3 The children saw the wave approaching and **broke into** a run.
4 I can see what you're **driving at**, but I don't think you fully understand.
5 Whenever her son returned from university he looked thin and unhealthy. 'He just needs **feeding up**', she reassured herself.
6 'Come on, Penny, you should come, too.' Penny **cast about for** any excuse to stay.
7 The two old neighbours **fell out** over a wall between their gardens.
8 Enthusiastic students have a tendency to **blurt out** the answers without putting up their hands.
9 Harriet refused to speak to me after I crashed the car, and we have never **made up** since.
10 Jamaica: a name that **conjures up** white sand and tropical beaches.

a) say something suddenly and without thinking
b) interrupt when someone is talking
c) start doing something
d) look for, or try to think of, something, especially when you feel pressure to do something quickly
e) *spoken phrase:* what you are really trying to say
f) *informal:* stop being friendly with someone because you have had a disagreement with them
g) give someone more food than usual in order to make them stronger or fatter
h) *spoken phrase:* leave a place
i) bring something such as a feeling or memory to your mind
j) become friendly with someone again after an argument

Main themes

Before you read the story, you may want to think about some of its main themes. The questions will help you think about the story as you are reading it for the first time. There is more discussion of the main themes in the *Literary analysis* section after the story.

Belonging

Wolf is not an ordinary pet and does not behave like other dogs do towards their owners. But Walt and Madge welcome him into their lives and try their best to make him a member of their family.

7 As you read the story, think about these questions:

a) Why do the Irvines treat the dog the way they do?

b) Why does the dog want to escape?

c) Why does he eventually accept the couple's kindness?

b) Does he really belong to the Irvines?

Choices

The story deals with choices that the characters have to make.

8 As you read, ask yourself:

a) What choices do the characters make in the story?

b) Which choices are difficult ones? Are any made without thinking?

c) Would you make the same choices?

Contrasts

Two very different worlds, and two very different approaches to owning a dog are described and contrasted in the story.

9 Think about these questions as you read:

a) What are the main features of both worlds?

b) In what way do the people treat the dog differently?

c) Which world do you think the dog is most attracted to?

Brown Wolf

by Jack London

She had delayed, because of the dew-wet grass, in order to put on her overshoes, and when she emerged from the house found her waiting husband absorbed in the wonder of a bursting almond-bud. She sent a questing[1] glance across the tall grass and in and out among the orchard trees.

'Where's Wolf?' she asked.

'He was here a moment ago.' Walt Irvine drew himself away with a **jerk** from the **metaphysics** and poetry of the organic miracle of blossom, and surveyed the landscape. 'He was running a rabbit the last I saw of him.'

'Wolf! Wolf! Here, Wolf!' she called, as they left the clearing and took the trail that led down through the waxen-belled manzanita[2] jungle to the county road.

Irvine thrust between his lips the little finger of each hand and lent to her efforts a **shrill** whistling.

She covered her ears hastily and made a **wry** grimace.

'My! for a poet, delicately **attuned** and all the rest of it, you can make unlovely noises. My eardrums are pierced. You outwhistle –'

'Orpheus[3].'

'I was about to say a street-arab,' she concluded severely.

'Poesy[4] does not prevent one from being practical – at least it doesn't prevent *me*. Mine is no **futility** of genius that can't sell **gems** to the magazines.'

He assumed a **mock extravagance**, and went on:

---

1 *literary*: looking for something
2 a small tree that grows in western North America, including California
3 in Greek mythology Orpheus was a legendary musician
4 *old-fashioned*: poetry

'I am no attic singer, no ballroom warbler[5]. And why? Because I am practical. Mine is no **squalor** of song that cannot **transmute** itself, with proper exchange value, into a flower-crowned cottage, a sweet mountain-meadow, a grove of redwoods, an orchard of thirty-seven trees, one long row of blackberries and two short rows of strawberries, to say nothing of a quarter of a mile of **gurgling** brook.'

'Oh, that all your song-transmutations were as successful!' she laughed.

'Name one that wasn't.'

'Those two beautiful **sonnets** that you transmuted into the cow that was accounted the worst milker in the township.'

'She was beautiful – 'he began.

'But she didn't give milk,' Madge interrupted.

'But she *was* beautiful, now, wasn't she?' he insisted.

'And here's where beauty and utility[6] fall out,' was her reply. 'And there's the Wolf!'

From the thicket-covered hillside came a crashing of underbrush, and then, forty feet above them, on the edge of the **sheer** wall of rock, appeared a wolf's head and shoulders. His braced forepaws dislodged a pebble, and with sharp-pricked ears and peering eyes he watched the fall of the pebble till it struck at their feet. Then he transferred his gaze and with open mouth laughed down at them.

'You Wolf, you!' and 'You blessed[7] Wolf!' the man and woman called out to him.

The ears flattened back and down at the sound, and the head seemed to snuggle under the caress of an invisible hand.

They watched him scramble backward into the thicket, then proceeded on their way. Several minutes later, rounding a turn in the trail where the descent was less **precipitous**, he joined them in the midst of a miniature avalanche of pebbles and loose soil. He was not demonstrative. A pat and a rub around the ears from the man, and a more prolonged caressing from the

5 *humorous*: someone who sings, but not very well
6 *formal*: the state of being useful
7 *literary*: used for emphasizing that you are annoyed about something

woman, and he was away down the trail in front of them, **gliding** effortlessly over the ground in true wolf fashion.

In build and coat and brush he was a huge timber-wolf[8]; but the **lie was given** to his wolf-hood by his color and marking. There the dog unmistakably advertised itself. No wolf was ever colored like him. He was brown, deep brown, red-brown, an **orgy** of browns. Back and shoulders were a warm brown that paled on the sides and underneath to a yellow that was **dingy** because of the brown that **lingered** in it. The white of the throat and paws and the spots over the eyes was dirty because of the persistent and ineradicable[9] brown, while the eyes themselves were twin **topazes**, golden and brown.

The man and woman loved the dog very much; perhaps this was because it had been such a task to win his love. It had been no easy matter when he first drifted in mysteriously out of nowhere to their little mountain cottage. Footsore and famished, he had killed a rabbit under their very noses and under their very windows, and then crawled away and slept by the spring at the foot of the blackberry bushes. When Walt Irvine went down to inspect the intruder, he was snarled at for his pains, and Madge likewise was snarled at when she went down to present, as a peace-offering, a large pan of bread and milk.

A most unsociable dog he proved to be, resenting all their **advances**, refusing to let them lay hands on him, menacing them with bared fangs and bristling hair. Nevertheless he remained, sleeping and resting by the spring, and eating the food they gave him after they set it down at a safe distance and retreated. His wretched physical condition explained why he lingered; and when he had recuperated, after several days' sojourn, he disappeared.

And this would have been the end of him, so far as Irvine and his wife were concerned, had not Irvine at that particular time been called away into the northern part of the state. Biding along on the train, near to the line between California

---

8   a subspecies of grey wolf
9   *formal*: impossible to get rid of

and Oregon, he chanced to look out of the window and saw his unsociable guest sliding along the wagon road, brown and wolfish, tired yet tireless, dust-covered and soiled[10] with two hundred miles of travel.

Now Irvine was a man of impulse, a poet. He got off the train at the next station, bought a piece of meat at a butcher shop, and captured the vagrant[11] on the outskirts of the town. The return trip was made in the baggage car[12], and so Wolf came a second time to the mountain cottage. Here he was tied up for a week and made love to by the man and woman. But it was very **circumspect** love-making. Remote and alien as a traveller from another planet, he snarled down their soft-spoken love-words. He never barked. In all the time they had him he was never known to bark.

To win him became a problem. Irvine liked problems. He had a metal plate made, on which was stamped: 'Return to Walt Irvine, Glen Ellen, Sonoma County, California.' This was **riveted** to a collar and strapped about the dog's neck. Then he was turned loose, and promptly he disappeared. A day later came a telegram[13] from Mendocino County. In twenty hours he had made over a hundred miles to the north, and was still going when captured.

He came back by Wells Fargo Express[14], was tied up three days, and was loosed on the fourth and lost. This time he gained southern Oregon before he was caught and returned. Always, as soon as he received his liberty, he **fled** away, and always he fled north. He was possessed of an obsession that drove him north. The **homing instinct**, Irvine called it, after he had expended the selling price of a sonnet in getting the animal back from northern Oregon.

Another time the brown wanderer succeeded in traversing half the length of California, all of Oregon, and most of

10 *formal*: dirty
11 *formal*: someone with no home or job
12 *US English*: the carriage of a train where passenger's bags are carried
13 *old-fashioned*: a message that was sent by telegraph (along a wire), used for short urgent messages
14 a mail delivery service that carried letters and other things in the west of the USA

Washington, before he was picked up and returned 'Collect.'[15] A remarkable thing was the speed with which he travelled. Fed up and rested, as soon as he was loosed he devoted all his energy to getting over the ground. On the first day's run he was known to cover as high as a hundred and fifty miles, and after that he would average a hundred miles a day until caught. He always arrived back lean and hungry and savage, and always departed fresh and **vigorous**, cleaving[16] his way northward in response to some prompting of his being that no one could understand.

But at last, after a futile year of flight, he accepted the inevitable and elected to remain at the cottage where first he had killed the rabbit and slept by the spring. Even after that, a long time elapsed before the man and woman succeeded in patting him. It was a great victory, for they alone were allowed to put hands on him. He was **fastidiously** exclusive, and no guest at the cottage ever succeeded in making up to him. A low growl greeted such approach; if anyone had the hardihood to come nearer, the lips lifted, the naked fangs appeared, and the growl became a snarl – a snarl so terrible and malignant that it **awed** the **stoutest** of them, as it likewise awed the farmers' dogs that knew ordinary dog snarling, but had never seen wolf snarling before.

He was without antecedents[17]. His history began with Walt and Madge. He had come up from the south, but never a clew[18] did they get of the owner from whom he had evidently fled. Mrs Johnson, their nearest neighbor and the one who supplied them with milk, proclaimed him a Klondike dog. Her brother was burrowing for frozen pay-streaks[19] in that far country, and so she constituted herself an authority on the subject.

But they did not dispute her. There were the tips of Wolf's ears, obviously so severely frozen at some time that they would

15 when a parcel is sent 'collect', the person receiving it pays for it on delivery
16 *literary*: to cut or break something into two parts with a lot of force. Here, the image is of cutting the land in two.
17 *formal*: a record of what happened or existed before that time
18 an old-fashioned spelling of *clue*
19 digging for gold. A 'pay-streak' is a valuable piece of rock containing a lot of gold.

never quite heal again. Besides, he looked like the photographs of the Alaskan dogs they saw published in magazines and newspapers. They often speculated over his past, and tried to conjure up (from what they had read and heard) what his northland life had been. That the northland still drew him, they knew; for at night they sometimes heard him crying softly; and when the north wind blew and the bite of frost was in the air, a great restlessness would come upon him and he would lift a mournful lament[20] which they knew to be the long wolf-howl. Yet he never barked. No provocation was great enough to draw from him that canine cry.

Long discussion they had, during the time of winning him, as to whose dog he was. Each claimed him, and each proclaimed loudly any expression of affection made by him. But the man had the better of it at first, chiefly because he was a man. It was **patent** that Wolf had had no experience with women. He did not understand women. Madge's skirts were something he never quite accepted. The **swish** of them was enough to set him a-bristle with suspicion, and on a windy day she could not approach him at all.

On the other hand, it was Madge who fed him; also it was she who ruled the kitchen, and it was by her favor, and her favor alone, that he was permitted to come within that sacred precinct[21]. It was because of these things that she bade fair[22] to overcome the handicap of her garments[23]. Then it was that Walt put forth[24] special effort, making it a practice to have Wolf lie at his feet while he wrote, and, between petting and talking, losing much time from his work. Walt won in the end, and his victory was most probably due to the fact that he was a man, though Madge averred that they would have had another quarter of a mile of gurgling brook, and at least two west winds sighing through their redwoods, had Walt properly devoted his energies

20 a song or poem in which sadness is expressed about a death or loss
21 *formal*: a place marked with limits such as walls
22 *literary*: was able to
23 *formal*: clothes
24 *literary*: made

to song-transmutation and left Wolf alone to exercise[25] a natural taste and an unbiased judgment.

'It's about time I heard from those triolets[26],' Walt said, after a silence of five minutes, during which they had swung steadily down the trail. 'There'll be a check[27] at the post office, I know, and we'll transmute it into beautiful buckwheat flour, a gallon of maple syrup, and a new pair of overshoes for you.'

'And into beautiful milk from Mrs Johnson's beautiful cow,' Madge added. 'To-morrow's the first of the month, you know.'

Walt **scowled** unconsciously; then his face brightened, and he clapped his hand to his breast pocket.

'Never mind. I have here a nice, beautiful, new cow, the best milker in California.'

'When did you write it?' she demanded eagerly. Then, reproachfully, 'And you never showed it to me.'

'I saved it to read to you on the way to the post office, in a spot remarkably like this one,' he answered, indicating, with a wave of his hand, a dry log on which to sit.

A tiny stream flowed out of a dense fern-brake, slipped down a mossy-lipped stone, and ran across the path at their feet. From the valley arose the mellow song of meadow larks, while about them, in and out, through sunshine and shadow, **fluttered** great yellow butterflies.

Up from below came another sound that broke in upon Walt reading softly from his **manuscript**. It was a crunching of heavy feet, punctuated now and again by the **clattering** of a displaced stone. As Walt finished and looked to his wife for approval, a man came into view around the turn of the trail. He was bare-headed and sweaty. With a handkerchief in one hand he mopped his face, while in the other hand he carried a new hat and a **wilted** starched collar[28] which he had removed from his

---

25 *formal*: to use your power or rights
26 a type of poem with eight lines
27 *US English*: an order to a bank to pay a stated amount of money; (*British English*: cheque)
28 in the past, shirts had removable collars. A substance called starch was used to keep them stiff.

neck. He was a well-built man, and his muscles seemed on the point of bursting out of the painfully new and ready-made black clothes he wore.

'Warm day,' Walt greeted him. Walt believed in country democracy[29], and never missed an opportunity to practice it.

The man paused and nodded.

'I guess I ain't used much to the warm,' he **vouchsafed** half apologetically. 'I'm more accustomed to zero weather.'

'You don't find any of that in this country,' Walt laughed.

'Should say not,' the man answered. 'An' I ain't here a-lookin' for it neither. I'm tryin' to find my sister. Mebbe you know where she lives. Her name's Johnson, Mrs William Johnson.'

'You're not her Klondike brother!' Madge cried, her eyes bright with interest, 'about whom we've heard so much?'

'Yes'm, that's me,' he answered modestly. 'My name's Miller, Skiff Miller. I just thought I'd s'prise her.'

'You are on the right track then. Only you've come by the footpath.' Madge stood up to direct him, pointing up the canyon a quarter of a mile. 'You see that blasted[30] redwood? Take the little trail turning off to the right. It's the short cut to her house. You can't miss it.'

'Yes'm, thank you, ma'am,' he said. He made **tentative** efforts to go, but seemed awkwardly **rooted to the spot**. He was gazing at her with an open admiration of which he was quite unconscious, and which was drowning, along with him, in the rising sea of embarrassment in which he **floundered**.

'We'd like to hear you tell about the Klondike,' Madge said. 'Mayn't we come over some day while you are at your sister's? Or, better yet, won't you come over and have dinner with us?'

'Yes'm, thank you, ma'am,' he **mumbled** mechanically. Then he caught himself up and added: 'I ain't stoppin' long. I got to be pullin' north again. I go out on to-night's train. You see, I've got a mail contract[31] with the government.'

29 treating everybody equally
30 *literary*: a blasted tree is damaged by storms, heat, or lightning
31 a job carrying mail from place to place

When Madge had said that it was **too bad**, he made another futile effort to go. But he could not take his eyes from her face. He forgot his embarrassment in his admiration, and it was her turn to **flush** and feel uncomfortable.

It was at this juncture[32], when Walt had just decided it was time for him to be saying something to relieve the strain, that Wolf, who had been away nosing through the brush, trotted wolf-like into view.

Skiff Miller's abstraction[33] disappeared. The pretty woman before him passed out of his field of vision. He had eyes only for the dog, and a great wonder came into his face.

'Well, I'll be hanged[34]!' he enunciated slowly and solemnly.

He sat down ponderingly[35] on the log, leaving Madge standing. At the sound of his voice, Wolf's ears had flattened down, then his mouth had opened in a laugh. He trotted slowly up to the stranger and first smelled his hands, then licked them with his tongue.

Skiff Miller patted the dog's head, and slowly and solemnly repeated, 'Well, I'll be damned!'

'Excuse me, ma'am,' he said the next moment, 'I was just s'prised some, that was all.'

'We're surprised, too,' she answered lightly. 'We never saw Wolf make up to a stranger before.'

'Is that what you call him – Wolf?' the man asked.

Madge nodded. 'But I can't understand his friendliness toward you – unless it's because you're from the Klondike. He's a Klondike dog, you know.'

'Yes'm,' Miller said absently. He lifted one of Wolf's forelegs and examined the footpads, pressing them and **denting** them with his thumb. 'Kind of soft,' he remarked. 'He ain't been on trail for a long time.'

32 *formal*: a stage in a process or activity
33 *formal*: distraction
34 *old-fashioned*: used for emphasizing how surprised or shocked you are about something
35 *formal*: in a way that shows you are thinking carefully about something

'I say,' Walt broke in, 'it is remarkable the way he lets you handle him.'

Skiff Miller arose, no longer awkward with admiration of Madge, and in a sharp, businesslike manner asked, 'How long have you had him?'

But just then the dog, squirming and rubbing against the newcomer's legs, opened his mouth and barked. It was an explosive bark, brief and joyous, but a bark.

'That's a new one on me,' Skiff Miller remarked.

Walt and Madge stared at each other. The miracle had happened. Wolf had barked.

'It's the first time he ever barked,' Madge said.

'First time I ever heard him, too,' Miller volunteered.

Madge smiled at him. The man was evidently a humorist.

'Of course,' she said, 'since you have only seen him for five minutes.'

Skiff Miller looked at her sharply, seeking in her face the guile[36] her words had led him to suspect.

'I thought you understood,' he said slowly. 'I thought you'd tumbled to it[37] from his makin' up to me. He's my dog. His name ain't Wolf. It's Brown.'

'Oh, Walt!' was Madge's instinctive cry to her husband.

Walt was on the defensive at once.

'How do you know he's your dog?' he demanded.

'Because he is,' was the reply.

'Mere assertion,' Walt said sharply.

In his slow and pondering way, Skiff Miller looked at him, then asked, with a nod of his head toward Madge:

'How d'you know she's your wife? You just say, 'Because she is,' and I'll say it's mere assertion. The dog's mine. I bred 'm an' raised 'm, an' I guess I ought to know. Look here. I'll prove it to you.'

Skiff Miller turned to the dog. 'Brown!' His voice rang out sharply, and at the sound the dog's ears flattened down as to a caress. 'Gee!' The dog made a swinging turn to the right. 'Now

36 *formal*: the skilful use of dishonest means to trick people or to make them do what you want
37 *informal*: understood

mush-on!' And the dog ceased his swing **abruptly** and started straight ahead, halting obediently at command.

'I can do it with whistles,' Skiff Miller said proudly. 'He was my lead dog.'

'But you are not going to take him away with you?' Madge asked tremulously[38].

The man nodded.

'Back into that awful Klondike world of suffering?'

He nodded and added: 'Oh, it ain't so bad as all that. Look at me. Pretty healthy specimen, ain't I!'

'But the dogs! The terrible hardship, the heart-breaking toil, the starvation, the frost! Oh, I've read about it and I know.'

'I nearly ate him once, over on Little Fish River,' Miller volunteered grimly. 'If I hadn't got a **moose** that day was all that saved 'm.'

'I'd have died first!' Madge cried.

'Things is different down here,' Miller explained. 'You don't have to eat dogs. You think different just about the time you're all in. You've never been all in, so you don't know anything about it.'

'That's the very point,' she argued warmly. 'Dogs are not eaten in California. Why not leave him here? He is happy. He'll never want for food – you know that. He'll never suffer from cold and hardship. Here all is softness and gentleness. Neither the human nor nature is savage. He will never know a whip-lash again. And as for the weather – why, it never snows here.'

'But it's all-fired hot in summer, beggin' your pardon[39],' Skiff Miller laughed.

'But you do not answer,' Madge continued passionately. 'What have you to offer him in that northland life?'

'Grub[40], when I've got it, and that's most of the time,' came the answer.

'And the rest of the time?'

38 literary: if your voice is tremulous, it is not steady, for example because you are afraid
39 *old-fashioned*: used for saying that you disagree with what someone has just said
40 *informal*: food

'No grub.'

'And the work?'

'Yes, plenty of work,' Miller blurted out impatiently. 'Work without end, an' famine, an' frost, an' all the rest of the miseries – that's what he'll get when he comes with me. But he likes it. He is used to it. He knows that life. He was born to it an' brought up to it. An' you don't know anything about it. You don't know what you're talking about. That's where the dog belongs, and that's where he'll be happiest.'

'The dog doesn't go,' Walt announced in a determined voice. 'So there is no need of further discussion.'

'What's that?' Skiff Miller demanded, big brows lowering and an **obstinate** flush of blood reddening his forehead.

'I said the dog doesn't go, and that settles it. I don't believe he's your dog. You may have seen him sometime. You may even sometime have driven him for his owner. But his obeying the ordinary driving commands of the Alaskan trail is no demonstration that he is yours. Any dog in Alaska would obey you as he obeyed. Besides, he is undoubtedly a valuable dog, as dogs go in Alaska, and that is sufficient explanation of your desire to get possession of him. Anyway, you've got to prove property.'

Skiff Miller, **cool and collected**, the obstinate flush a trifle[41] deeper on his forehead, his huge muscles bulging under the black cloth of his coat, carefully looked the poet up and down as though measuring the strength of his slenderness.

The Klondiker's face took on a contemptuous expression as he said finally: 'I reckon there's nothin' in sight to prevent me takin' the dog right here an' now.'

Walt's face reddened, and the striking-muscles of his arms and shoulders seemed to stiffen and grow tense. His wife fluttered apprehensively into the breach[42].

'Maybe Mr Miller is right,' she said. 'I am afraid that he is. Wolf does seem to know him, and certainly he answers to the

41 *formal*: slightly
42 *literary*: if someone steps in the breach they are trying to help someone, or to do someone's job for them when they are unable to do it

name of 'Brown.' He made friends with him instantly, and you know that's something he never did with anybody before. Besides, look at the way he barked. He was just bursting with joy. Joy over what? Without doubt at finding Mr Miller.'

Walt's striking-muscles relaxed, and his shoulders seemed to **droop** with hopelessness.

'I guess you're right, Madge,' he said. 'Wolf isn't Wolf, but Brown, and he must belong to Mr Miller.'

'Perhaps Mr Miller will sell him,' she suggested. 'We can buy him.'

Skiff Miller shook his head, no longer **belligerent**, but kindly, quick to be generous in response to generousness.

'I had five dogs,' he said, casting about for the easiest way to temper[43] his refusal. 'He was the leader. They was the crack team of Alaska. Nothin' could touch 'em. In 1898 I refused five thousand dollars for the bunch. Dogs was high, then, anyway; but that wasn't what made the fancy price. It was the team itself. Brown was the best in the team. That winter I refused twelve hundred for 'm. I didn't sell 'm then, an' I ain't a-sellin' 'm now. Besides, I think a mighty lot of that dog. I've been lookin' for 'm for three years. It made me fair sick when I found he'd been stole – not the value of him, but the – well, I liked 'm so, that's all. I couldn't believe my eyes when I seen 'm just now. I thought I was dreamin'. It was too good to be true. Why, I was his nurse. I put 'm to bed, snug every night. His mother died, and I brought 'm up on condensed milk at two dollars a can when I couldn't afford it in my own coffee. He never knew any mother but me. He used to suck my finger regular, the darn[44] little pup – that finger right there!'

And Skiff Miller, too **overwrought** for speech, held up a forefinger for them to see.

'That very finger,' he managed to articulate, as though it somehow **clinched** the proof of ownership and the bond of affection.

43 *formal*: to make something less strong or extreme
44 *old-fashioned*: used for emphasizing what you are saying

He was still gazing at his extended finger when Madge began to speak.

'But the dog,' she said. 'You haven't considered the dog.'

Skiff Miller looked puzzled.

'Have you thought about him?' she asked.

'Don't know what you're drivin' at,' was the response.

'Maybe the dog has some choice in the matter,' Madge went on. 'Maybe he has his likes and desires. You have not considered him. You give him no choice. It has never entered your mind that possibly he might prefer California to Alaska. You consider only what you like. You do with him as you would with a sack of potatoes or a bale of hay[45].'

This was a new way of looking at it, and Miller was visibly impressed as he debated it in his mind. Madge took advantage of his indecision.

'If you really love him, what would be happiness to him would be your happiness also,' she urged.

Skiff Miller continued to debate with himself, and Madge stole a glance of exultation[46] to her husband, who looked back warm approval.

'What do you think?' the Klondiker suddenly demanded.

It was her turn to be puzzled. 'What do you mean?' she asked.

'D'ye think he'd sooner stay in California!'

She nodded her head with positiveness. 'I am sure of it.'

Skiff Miller again debated with himself, though this time aloud, at the same time running his gaze in a judicial way over the mooted[47] animal.

'He was a good worker. He's done a heap of work for me. He never loafed[48] on me, an' he was a joe-dandy at hammerin' a raw team into shape[49]. He's got a head on him. He can do everything but talk. He knows what you say to him. Look at 'm now. He knows we're talkin' about him.'

45 a large quantity of dried grass tied tightly for storing
46 *formal*: a feeling or show of great pleasure and excitement, especially about something that you have achieved
47 *unusual*: something that is mooted is being discussed
48 *informal*: spend time doing nothing, usually when you should be working
49 he was very good at getting a new team ready for sledding

The dog was lying at Skiff Miller's feet, head close down on paws, ears erect and listening, and eyes that were quick and eager to follow the sound of speech as it fell from the lips of first one and then the other.

'An' there's a lot of work in 'm yet. He's good for years to come. An' I do like him.'

Once or twice after that Skiff Miller opened his mouth and closed it again without speaking. Finally he said:

'I'll tell you what I'll do. Your remarks, ma'am, has some weight in them. The dog's worked hard, and maybe he's earned a soft berth an' has got a right to choose. Anyway, we'll leave it up to him. Whatever he says, goes. You people stay right here settin' down. I'll say good-by and walk off casual-like. If he wants to stay, he can stay. If he wants to come with me, let 'm come. I won't call 'm to come an' don't you call 'm to come back.'

He looked with sudden suspicion at Madge, and added, 'Only you must play fair. No persuadin' after my back is turned.'

'We'll play fair,' Madge began, but Skiff Miller broke in on her assurances.

'I know the ways of women,' he announced. 'Their hearts is soft. When their hearts is touched they're likely to stack the cards, look at the bottom of the deck[50], an' lie – beggin' your pardon, ma'am. I'm only discoursin' about women in general.'

'I don't know how to thank you,' Madge **quavered**.

'I don't see as you've got any call to thank me,' he replied. 'Brown ain't decided yet. Now you won't mind if I go away slow! It's no more'n fair, seein' I'll be out of sight inside a hundred yards.' – Madge agreed, and added, 'And I promise you faithfully that we won't do anything to influence him.'

'Well, then, I might as well be gettin' along,' Skiff Miller said in the ordinary tones of one departing.

At this change in his voice, Wolf lifted his head quickly, and still more quickly got to his feet when the man and woman shook hands. He sprang up on his hind legs, resting his fore paws on

50 he uses the metaphor of playing cards to describe how women cheat when they are emotional

her hip and at the same time licking Skiff Miller's hand. When the latter shook hands with Walt, Wolf repeated his act, resting his weight on Walt and licking both men's hands.

'It ain't no picnic, I can tell you that,' were the Klondiker's last words, as he turned and went slowly up the trail.

For the distance of twenty feet Wolf watched him go, himself all eagerness and expectancy, as though waiting for the man to turn and retrace his steps. Then, with a quick low whine, Wolf sprang after him, overtook him, caught his hand between his teeth with reluctant **tenderness**, and **strove** gently to make him pause.

Failing in this, Wolf raced back to where Walt Irvine sat, catching his coat-sleeve in his teeth and trying **vainly** to drag him after the retreating man.

Wolf's **perturbation** began to wax[51]. He desired ubiquity[52]. He wanted to be in two places at the same time, with the old master and the new, and steadily the distance between them was increasing. He sprang about excitedly, making short nervous leaps and twists, now toward one, now toward the other, in painful indecision, not knowing his own mind, desiring both and unable to choose, uttering quick sharp whines and beginning to pant.

He sat down abruptly on his **haunches**, thrusting his nose upward, the mouth opening and closing with jerking movements, each time opening wider. These jerking movements were in unison with the recurrent **spasms** that attacked the throat, each spasm severer and more intense than the preceding one. And in accord with jerks and spasms the larynx[53] began to vibrate, at first silently, accompanied by the rush of air expelled from the lungs, then sounding a low, deep note, the lowest in the register of the human ear. All this was the nervous and muscular preliminary to howling.

---

51 *literary*: become bigger or stronger
52 *formal*: able to be present everywhere
53 *medical*: the organ in your throat that contains your vocal cords, which produce sounds

But just as the howl was on the verge of bursting from the full throat, the wide-opened mouth was closed, the paroxysms[54] ceased, and he looked long and steadily at the retreating man. Suddenly Wolf turned his head, and over his shoulder just as steadily regarded Walt. The appeal was unanswered. Not a word nor a sign did the dog receive, no suggestion and no clew as to what his conduct should be.

A glance ahead to where the old master was nearing the curve of the trail excited him again. He sprang to his feet with a whine, and then, struck by a new idea, turned his attention to Madge. Hitherto[55] he had ignored her, but now, both masters failing him, she alone was left. He went over to her and snuggled his head in her lap, nudging her arm with his nose – an old trick of his when begging for favors. He backed away from her and began writhing and twisting playfully, curvetting and prancing[56], half rearing and striking his forepaws to the earth, struggling with all his body, from the **wheedling** eyes and flattening ears to the wagging tail, to express the thought that was in him and that was denied him utterance[57].

This, too, he soon abandoned. He was depressed by the coldness of these humans who had never been cold before. No response could he draw from them, no help could he get. They did not consider him. They were as dead.

He turned and silently gazed after the old master. Skiff Miller was rounding the curve. In a moment he would be gone from view. Yet he never turned his head, **plodding** straight onward, slowly and methodically, as though possessed of no interest in what was occurring behind his back.

And in this fashion he went out of view. Wolf waited for him to reappear. He waited a long minute, silently, quietly, without

---

54 *formal*: a sudden uncontrolled expression of emotion
55 *formal*: until the present time
56 if a horse curvets, it jumps gracefully and energetically; if it prances it walks with lively steps, raising its legs high
57 *formal*: the expression of a thought in words

movement, as though turned to stone – withal[58] stone quick with eagerness and desire. He barked once, and waited. Then he turned and trotted back to Walt Irvine. He sniffed his hand and dropped down heavily at his feet, watching the trail where it curved emptily from view.

The tiny stream slipping down the mossy-lipped stone seemed suddenly to increase the volume of its gurgling noise. Save for the meadow larks, there was no other sound. The great yellow butterflies drifted silently through the sunshine and lost themselves in the **drowsy** shadows. Madge gazed triumphantly at her husband.

A few minutes later Wolf got upon his feet. Decision and deliberation marked his movements. He did not glance at the man and woman. His eyes were fixed up the trail. He had made up his mind. They knew it. And they knew, so far as they were concerned, that the ordeal had just begun.

He broke into a trot, and Madge's lips **pursed**, forming an avenue for the caressing sound that it was the will of her to send forth[59]. But the caressing sound was not made. She was impelled[60] to look at her husband, and she saw the **sternness** with which he watched her. The pursed lips relaxed, and she sighed inaudibly.

Wolf's trot broke into a run. Wider and wider were the leaps he made. Not once did he turn his head, his wolf's brush standing out straight behind him. He cut sharply across the curve of the trail and was gone.

---

58 *old-fashioned*: an old word meaning 'besides', here used with the meaning of 'even if'

59 she wants to make a noise that will attract Wolf back to them

60 *formal*: if a feeling or idea impels you to do something, it forces you to do it

Post-reading activities

Understanding the story

Use these questions to help you check that you have understood the story.

Walt, Madge and Wolf

1 What is Walt doing when Madge comes out of the house?
2 What does Walt do to call Wolf? Why is Madge not happy?
3 Why does Walt call his poetry practical? How does the story about the cow go against what Walt is saying?
4 How does Wolf respond to their calls?
5 How is Wolf like a wolf? How is he like a dog?
6 Why are the Irvines so fond of Wolf?
7 How long did Wolf stay at their house the first time? Why that long?
8 Approximately how many times does Wolf escape north, do you think?
9 What evidence is there for Mrs Johnson's theory that Wolf is from the Klondike?
10 Why does Walt have a greater claim to Wolf than Madge?
11 What price do the Irvines pay for the time Walt spends on Wolf, according to his wife?
12 What has Walt just started to read to Madge when Skiff appears? Why does he call it 'a nice, beautiful, new cow'?

Skiff

13 Why does the man approaching them seem uncomfortable?
14 Why do the strangers stay talking so long before Wolf arrives, without Skiff continuing on his journey?
15 What is the reason for Madge and Walt's surprise when Wolf arrives?
16 How do Madge and Walt react to the news that Wolf belongs to Skiff?
17 What is Madge's main concern?
18 Does Skiff argue against Madge's argument? What is his argument?
19 What is Walt's argument? Why does it not work?
20 How does Madge prevent the men from fighting?
21 Why won't Skiff sell him?
22 How does Madge persuade Skiff to change his mind?
23 As part of Skiff's plan, what must Walt and Madge do and not do in order to keep it fair for Skiff?

24 What has Wolf been doing all the time the people have been talking? How does he react when he realises that Skiff is leaving?
25 What does Wolf feel as Skiff walks away? What different strategies does he try?
26 How does Madge begin to react when she sees Wolf starting to move? Why does she stop?

Language study

Grammar

Fronting

The normal word order of sentences in English is subject + verb + object or complement, and if an adverbial phrase is included, this often comes last. However, it is often possible to change the order of these and, for example, start a sentence with an object or adverb. This is called 'fronting'. One effect of fronting is to emphasize different information in the sentence.

Look at this pair of sentences. Notice the change in word order and how the complement (*a most unsociable dog*) is emphasized.

> *He proved to be a most unsociable dog. (normal word order)*
> *A most unsociable dog he proved to be. (the complement is fronted)*

Fronting is also used to lend writing a formal style. This is particularly common in older writing of the 19th and early 20th century. If it is used today, it may sound old-fashioned.

1 **Look at the extracts (1–4) from the story. In which of these extracts:**
   a) **is the object fronted?**
   b) **are an adverb or adverbial phrase fronted?**
   c) **are both fronted?**
   d) **does the sentence sound particularly old-fashioned?**

1 *In all the time they had him he was never known to bark.*
2 *Long discussion they had.*
3 *This, too, he soon abandoned.*
4 *He ... elected to remain at the cottage where first he had killed the rabbit and slept by the spring.*

Inversion after fronting

2 Compare extracts (1–4) in exercise 1 with the following extract. How many examples of fronting are there? What do you notice about the subject-verb word order?

From the valley arose the mellow song of meadow larks, while about them, in and out, through sunshine and shadow, fluttered great yellow butterflies.

Up from below came another sound that broke in upon Walt reading softly from his manuscript.

This is called inversion and it has the effect of sounding particularly formal or literary. It may also sound very old-fashioned.

3 Rewrite the extract in exercise 3 above without any fronting. Compare the original with your text. Which has a more literary style? Which has a more modern style?

Inversion with fronting of negative adverbials

When an adverb has a negative meaning, we have to change the order of the subject and the verb. The structure is formal in style and usually only used in writing.

Look at these examples from the story. Notice the inversion of the subject and verb.

Not a word nor a sign did the dog receive.

No response could he draw from them, no help could he get.

… but never a clew did they get of the owner from whom he had evidently fled.

Not once did he turn his head.

4 Complete the sentences (1–4) so that they mean the same as the sentences in the extracts in exercise 3.

1 The dog .... a word or a sign.
2 He .... any response from them. He .... help.
3 They .... of the owner from whom he had fled.
4 He .... his head once.

5 Which sentences are more emphatic, those in the extracts in exercise 3 or the sentences you wrote for exercise 4? What is being emphasised?

6 Rewrite the sentences, using the adverbs given.

1 She could hardly approach him.
Hardly …

....

2 They couldn't afford a cow of their own under any circumstances.
Under no circumstances …

....

3 Skiff hadn't seen Wolf for more than three years.
Not for more than three years …

....

4 Wolf hadn't ever been faced with such a difficult choice before.
Never …

....

Vocabulary

Common expressions

7 Look at the common expressions from the story (1–10) and match them with their definitions (a–j).

1 **as/so far as … is concerned**
Wolf disappears from their lives for the first time.
*And this would have been the end of him, **so far as** Irvine and his wife **were concerned** …*

2 **better still/yet**
Madge wants to hear all about Klondike life.
*'Mayn't we come over while you are at your sister's? Or, **better yet**, won't you come over and have dinner with us?'*

3 **for your pains**
Walt is trying to help an angry Wolf.
*When Walt Irvine went down to inspect the intruder, he was snarled at **for his pains** …*

4 **I'd sooner do something**
Skiff asks Madge what she thinks Wolf prefers.
*'D'ye think he'**d sooner** stay in California!'*

5 **leave it up to someone**
Skiff plans how it will be decided.
*'Anyway, we'll **leave it up to** him. Whatever he says, goes.'*

6 **on the verge of**
Is Wolf going to howl?
*Just as the howl was **on the verge of** bursting from the full throat, the wide-opened mouth was closed …*

7 **out of nowhere**
Wolf's arrival is being described.
*It had been no easy matter when he first drifted in mysteriously **out of nowhere** to their little mountain cottage.*

8 **save for**
There is very little noise.
***Save for** the meadow larks, there was no other sound.*

9 **a new one on me**
No one has ever heard Wolf bark before.
*'That's **a new one on me**,' Skiff Miller remarked.*

10 **think highly/a lot of someone**
Skiff is explaining why he won't sell Wolf.
*'Besides, I **think a mighty lot of that dog**.'*

a) about to do something or experience something
b) appearing, arriving, happening, etc quickly or unexpectedly
c) except for
d) let someone else make the decision
e) admire and respect someone a lot
f) used for emphasizing that you have not been properly rewarded for your efforts
g) used for saying what you would prefer to do
h) used for saying your opinion about something, especially when this might be different from other people's opinions or the actual truth
i) used for talking about something you have never experienced or heard of before
j) used when you are adding a new idea that you think is better than a good one already mentioned

8 **Use the expressions (1–10) in exercise 7 to complete these sentences (a–j).**

a When she retired after 30 years working with the company, all she got .... was a box of chocolates.

b 'Do you want to go out to eat?' '......................... stay in, actually.'

c 'Do you want to stay or go?' 'I'll ....'

d They all seem to .... of her and talk about the quality of her work a lot.
e 'Have you ever tasted a fruit like this one?' 'No, it's.......................... '
f He didn't get the grades he needed so that's the end of university
   ....
g It was so fast. The car seemed to come ....
h The room was completely dark, ... one candle burning in the corner.
i The two countries were .... war.
j With that money you could fly to New York or, ...
   Tokyo!

Literary analysis

Plot

1 Write a one-sentence summary of the plot.
2 Here are some of the events in the story. They are in chronological order (the order in which they happened). In what order are they told in the story?
   Skiff raises the young puppy.
   Wolf arrives at the Irvine house.
   He runs away back towards the north.
   Walt captures him.
   Wolf decides to stay in California with the Irvines.
   The Irvines leave their house with Wolf to go to the post office. They meet Skiff.
   Wolf decides to leave the Irvines and go with Skiff.
3 Look at the list again in question 2. Can you add any more key events?
4 Why doesn't Walt just tie Wolf up rather than spending lots of time and money searching for him each time he escapes?
5 Skiff's arrival in the lives of the Irvines marks a turning point in the story. What is the majority of the story about before his arrival? What is the main focus afterwards?
6 Clearly, Skiff and Wolf's reunion is a very strange coincidence. Do you feel that this is acceptable to readers?
7 We are told that Walt and Madge 'loved the dog very much'. Does Skiff love Wolf, do you think? Is his love similar to the Irvines' love? And what about the dog? How does he feel about his 'masters'?

8 Read about the argument between Skiff and the Irvines again
   (pages 148–53, starting *'Of course,' she said, since you've only seen
   him for five minutes ...'* down to *'I'll tell you what I'll do.'*). Put these
   arguments from both sides in the order in which they are used.

Arguments for Wolf to go with Skiff
1 Canada is where he belongs.
2 His bark is clearly a sign that he is happy to see Skiff.
3 It is hot in the summer in California.
4 Saying that something or someone belongs to you must mean
   something.
5 The dog behaves in a friendly way to him.
6 The dog belongs to him.
7 The dog responds to his commands.
8 Walt and Madge cannot stop Skiff from taking him if he wants.

Arguments for Wolf to stay with Madge and Walt
9 Dogs are not eaten in California!
10 He will never get cold.
11 Life is very difficult for dogs in the north.
12 Saying something belongs to you does not mean it is true.
13 Skiff may have financial reasons for claiming that Wolf belongs to
    him.
14 The ability to control a sled dog is not proof of ownership.
15 Wolf will never be hungry in California.

9 Look at the arguments in question 2 again. Are they always used
   by the people that they favour, or does anyone ever introduce an
   argument against their own position. Why?
10 Why do you think Madge is so sure that Wolf will choose
    California? What does she fail to understand about Wolf's
    motivation?
11 Is Skiff's plan to let Wolf choose fair in your opinion? Why? Why
    not? How else could they have asked him to choose?
12 At the end of the story we are told that for Walt and Madge, 'the
    ordeal had just begun'. What ordeal do they face?
13 What is the main message of the story, in your opinion? Would the
    message be different if Wolf had decided to stay with the Irvines?

Character

14 We are first introduced to Walt and Madge as they are having an argument about money and spending. What does the nature and style of their argument tell you about their relationship? Are they happy together, do you think?

15 Walt and Madge live in the countryside but they do not rely on nature for a living, as a farmer or gold digger does. What is their attitude to nature?

16 How would you describe Walt's personality? Think about the way he talks, his work and his relationship with Madge.

17 During the discussion with Skiff, who does most of the talking, Walt or Madge? Does Walt's behaviour with Skiff change your impression of Walt at all? How?

18 We learn more about Madge from the discussion with Skiff. What personal qualities does she show that we haven't seen until now?

19 Physically, the two men in the story are very different. In what other ways are they different?

20 Considering Skiff's life, why do you think he reacts so strongly to Madge's presence when they first meet?

21 When did Skiff's affection for Wolf start? How is this similar to the reasons that Walt and Madge are fond of him?

Animals in the story

22 Read the paragraph describing Wolf's physical appearance (beginning *In build and coat...*, page 141). How many different ways does the story teller use to talk about the fact that he is brown? What effect does this have on the imagined appearance of Wolf?

23 How do the dog's two names reflect how the people view him?

24 What parallels can be made between Madge and Walt's relationship with Wolf and a parent's relationship with a child? Is this a useful parallel to make, do you think? Why?

25 How does Wolf change through living with Walt and Madge? Is this change a permanent one that Skiff will notice, in your opinion?

26 Think of three adjectives to describe Wolf's character. What evidence do you have that he is like this?

27 What does Wolf's bark signify in the story? Why do you think he barks at that point in the story?

28 From what you know about how dogs behave and move, how realistic is Wolf as a dog? What does he do that makes you think this?

Narration

29 The story is told from the point of view of Walt and Madge Irvine. How would the story be different if it was told from Skiff's point of view?

30 If Wolf could tell his story, what do you think he would talk about most: his time as a puppy; his feelings towards the people in the story; his adventures as a sled dog; his travels north and south; the decision he has to make; something else? What are the most significant moments for him, do you think?

31 Look at the part of the story that tells of Wolf's many journeys north (beginning *A most unsociable dog ...*, down to '*But at last, ...*' pages 141–143). How long is the description of the first journey? And the second and the third? What effect does this have?

32 Through most of the story our impression of Wolf comes from the things he does, his behaviour and his body language. Read the following paragraph. What is the 'thought that is in him'? How does his behaviour tell us what he is thinking?

He went over to her and snuggled his head in her lap, nudging her arm with his nose – an old trick of his when begging for favors. He backed away from her and began writhing and twisting playfully, curvetting and prancing, half rearing and striking his forepaws to the earth, struggling with all his body, from the wheedling eyes and flattening ears to the wagging tail, to express the thought that was in him and that was denied him utterance.

33 How is the following paragraph different in terms of how it conveys Wolf's thoughts and feelings? Does this help to understand Wolf's final decision?

This, too, he soon abandoned. He was depressed by the coldness of these humans who had never been cold before. No response could he draw from them, no help could he get. They did not consider him. They were as dead.

34 In the story, do we get any impression of the story teller's attitudes:
    a) to Wolf, or dogs in general?
    b) to the rights and wrongs of the two options for Wolf?

Style

35 Read the first paragraph of the story again (page 139). Look at the words used to describe the landscape and natural world around the Irvines' cottage. What words and elements in the description suggest that nature is a positive force in their lives?

36 Walt describes their home and the land where they live in slightly different terms when he explains what he has exchanged for the money he has earned:

'... a flower-crowned cottage, a sweet mountain-meadow, a grove of redwoods, an orchard of thirty-seven trees, one long row of blackberries and two short rows of strawberries, to say nothing of a quarter of a mile of gurgling brook.'

How does he convey the generosity of nature here? Who would normally talk about property in this way? Whose style of speech is he imitating?

37 Walt describes the idea of using money to buy possessions as 'transmutation'. Why is this choice of language significant?

38 Later, Madge says about nature: 'Here all is softness and gentleness'. Read this extract out loud. What sounds are repeated that help to convey nature's softness? What words and images suggest gentleness?

A tiny stream flowed out of a dense fern-brake, slipped down a mossy-lipped stone, and ran across the path at their feet. From the valley arose the mellow song of meadow larks, while about them, in and out, through sunshine and shadow, fluttered great yellow butterflies.

39 Read the paragraph in question 38 silently this time. Focus on the sounds of nature that it describes and imagine hearing them. Now read the paragraph that follows this one in the story, on page 145 (beginning 'Up from below came another sound ...'). How is this important moment in the story marked by sound?

40 How is nature in the north described later in the story, when Madge is arguing with Skiff? How does the contrast with the landscape around the Irvine's house contribute to the themes of the story?

Imitating speech

Walt and Madge speak using very 'correct' English, with standard grammar. Skiff's speech is notable because of the attempt the writer has made to show special grammatical and phonological features of this man's spoken English in the way it is written.

41 Read the extract, which is where Skiff is talking about Wolf's sledding past. Find the non-standard features of English (a–f):
a) the subject and the verb not agreeing
b) the beginnings of words not being pronounced
c) the ends of words not being pronounced
d) non-standard negative forms
e) adjectives being used as adverbs
f) non-standard past forms

> 'In 1898 I refused five thousand dollars for the bunch. Dogs was high, then, anyway; but that wasn't what made the fancy price. It was the team itself. Brown was the best in the team. That winter I refused twelve hundred for 'm. I didn't sell 'm then, an' I ain't a-sellin' 'm now. Besides, I think a mighty lot of that dog. I've been lookin' for 'm for three years. It made me fair sick when I found he'd been stole – not the value of him, but the – well, I liked 'm so, that's all. I couldn't believe my eyes when I seen 'm just now. I thought I was dreamin'.'

Guidance to the above literary terms, answer keys to all the exercises and activities, plus a wealth of other reading-practice material, can be found at: www.macmillanenglish.com/readers.

My Family and Other Animals
(an extract)
by Gerald Durrell

About the author

Gerald Durrell had many jobs in his life, from zookeeper to television presenter. Although he is most widely known for his numerous books, 'author' is probably the job title he was least comfortable with. He devoted his whole life to animals, working simultaneously as a naturalist, zoo owner and conservationist for most of his seventy years. Writing for him was simply a way to raise money for his wildlife projects, of which there were many.

He was born in 1925 in India, but when his father died, the family moved to England. Louisa and her children Lawrence, Leslie, Margo and Gerald, tried to be happy there, but failed. For seven years they struggled under the grey skies of London. Gerald was miserable at school and frequently pretended to be sick to stay at home.

His eldest brother Lawrence, who became a famous writer himself, decided to move to Corfu, one of the Greek islands. It did not take him long to persuade the rest of the family to follow. So in 1935, when Gerald was 10 years old, the family emigrated, renting a large villa in the countryside, bathed in the Mediterranean sunshine and surrounded by olive groves. Gerald didn't go to school but his family organized teachers to come to the house. None of them had much luck with the boy. His real education was outside, studying the animals and plants in their garden, and it was this, not books, that fired his imagination. One man who did have a great influence on him was the doctor and academic, Theodore Stephanides, who lived on Corfu. The two became great friends and shared their passion for the wildlife of the island. Gerald made exciting discoveries about the natural world and Theodore helped him develop his skills as an amateur naturalist.

When war broke out in 1939, the family was forced to return to London. As a teenager, Gerald continued to be involved with animals, working in an aquarium and a pet shop. After the war, he got a job at a zoo. What he really wanted, though, was to go on wildlife collecting expeditions, ambitious trips around the world to capture animals to sell to zoos. He got his first chance in 1947, going to Cameroon as a junior expedition member. On future trips he was in charge, which meant he could make important decisions. His main concern was not making money. Instead of collecting large numbers of popular species, as other collectors did, Gerald made sure that they didn't collect too many individuals from a species and that the animals they had were well looked after. This unconventional attitude lost a lot of money and lost him his job at the zoo.

His next job was at an aquarium in Manchester. It was here that he met his first wife, Jacqueline, and it was she who encouraged him to write, which he did in order to make money for future expeditions. The success of his first book helped to raise the funds for his fourth expedition. The second book, from which the extract you are going to read is taken, My Family and Other Animals, brought him international recognition as a writer and a naturalist. It also funded expedition number five.

'Zoo' was Gerald's first word when he was a baby. His ambition was to own his own zoo because he was unhappy that most zoos were not designed for the animals but for people's entertainment. He believed their role should be for conservation, to look after endangered species in order to save them from extinction. After a lot of difficulty and two more expeditions, he found a site for his zoo on Jersey, an island between England and France. The Jersey Zoological Park (now Durrell Wildlife Park) opened to the public in 1959.

Over the next few decades, Durrell's zoo was at the centre of a revolution in zoo management, leading the way in conservation programmes that encouraged breeding endangered species in captivity. He led projects to protect species in their native habitats, too, in places like Madagascar and Mauritius.

All this hard work had an effect on his health and on his personal life. Jacqueline and he divorced in 1979. He then married Lee McGeorge Wilson, a zoologist who has run the Durrell Wildlife Conservation Trust since Gerald's death in 1995.

Gerald Durrell claimed that he didn't enjoy writing. Yet he authored 26 autobiographical books about his work, which are full of humour and a love for animals, as well as many other types of literature, including horror stories, children's novels, picture books, magazine articles and wildlife guides. He also made television series and films, all promoting care for the wild.

His impact on animal conservation is clear to see in the many places he is remembered: zoo centres are named after him; many of the babies of endangered species born in captivity are called Gerald or Gerry; awards are given in his name; there is a Durrell park in Corfu and statues have been erected of him. There is even an island near St Lucia that may soon be called Durrell Island! It is where Gerald's organization managed to save a species of lizard from extinction. Several newly-discovered species have been given the Latin name *durrelli*. Most important of all, there are many species whose future looks more certain because of Gerald Durrell.

About the extract

My Family and Other Animals was Gerald's second book, published in 1956. It is autobiographical, focusing on the four years he and his family spent on Corfu. It is a light-hearted account that mixes his passion for wildlife with the humour of growing up in an unusual family in extraordinary circumstances. It has been translated into many languages and has been read by millions of adults and children alike. There is a television series and two feature-length films based on the story.

The extract you are going to read comes from near the beginning of the book. It starts some way into Chapter Two and finishes at the end of Chapter Three. It describes the young Gerald's first adventures on the island of Corfu and introduces us to some colourful local characters, as well as many interesting animals.

Background information

Corfu

Corfu is one of the largest Greek islands in the Ionian Sea between Greece and Italy. Corfu has an important place in the history and mythology of Greece, but for many years it was ruled by foreign forces: Italians, then the French under Napoleon and finally the British, before unifying with Greece in 1864. Britain gained control of Corfu from the French in 1807 during the Napoleonic Wars and used it as a strategic naval base throughout the 19th century. During this time, many aspects of island life were improved. The British modernized the island's road system and introduced the British system of education. The islanders adopted a few English customs such as afternoon tea and cricket, and most islanders viewed British rule and culture as a positive influence.

The story is set in the 1930s, when the island was a very quiet place. The only industries were fishing and small-scale farming. An important crop was olives and the production of olive oil was a major industry. Wine was also produced, though most of it was for local consumption only. Meat and cheese came from the goatherds living on the island. Nowadays, these activities are much less important than Corfu's main industry: tourism. Foreigners are attracted to the island by its beautiful scenery and gorgeous beaches. Many people visit after reading *My Family and Other Animals*.

Summary

It may help you to know something about what happens in the extract before you read it. Don't worry, this summary does not tell you how the extract ends!

It is 1935 and the Durrells have just moved to the Greek island of Corfu. Each member of the family immediately starts to make themselves at home. Their mother enjoys cooking and gardening. Larry, the eldest son, now in his twenties, dedicates himself to writing novels. The children each follow their own interests. For Gerald, the youngest, there is nothing more fascinating than the huge variety of animals and plants in the garden.

At first he is so excited by the incredible activity of all the creatures that he cannot focus on one thing. There are distractions everywhere: in the air, under rocks and leaves, inside flowers. Gradually, though, he learns how to observe all these creatures and learn from them. He finds out interesting things about the animals, such as how they change colour, hunt or reproduce (produce offspring). He is always accompanied by Roger, the family dog, who shares with Gerald a love of the outdoors.

He slowly starts to look further, outside the garden, to the larger world around him. Local people pass by and say hello, offering him fruit and other gifts. He finds that their strange language becomes more and more familiar and after a while he is able to communicate in Greek. Each day after breakfast, Gerald and Roger go off on more adventures. They explore the olive groves of the local countryside and get to know the neighbours, meeting some interesting people on their travels. An old lady called Agathi teaches Gerald Greek songs. They make friends with Yani, a local goatherd, who gives Gerald lots of advice.

Occasionally, he meets a very mysterious man who he calls the 'Rose-beetle Man'. This fairy-tale figure is dressed in extraordinary clothes and carries with him many strange and wonderful objects and animals which he shows to Gerald. Gerald buys from him a young tortoise that he takes home as a pet. 'Achilles', as he is named, enjoys human company and becomes a member of the family. Achilles is the first of a series of unusual pets that Gerald adopts. But not all of them are as popular as Achilles. Gerald's habit of bringing creatures into the house starts to really annoy the rest of the family.

Pre-reading activities

Key vocabulary

This section will help you familiarize yourself with some of the more specific vocabulary used in the extract. You may want to use it to help you before you start reading, or as a revision exercise after you have finished the extract.

Animals in the story: verbs of movement

The writer closely observes the animals as they go about their daily lives, and he tries to accurately convey the way they behave, including how they move.

1 **Look at the sentences (1–13) below (don't worry if you don't understand the words in bold, just try to understand the general meaning). Match the animals in the box with the sentences.**

ant	bird	cat	cockroach	cow	crab	dog
elephant	frog	hippopotamus	penguin	snake	tiger	

1 Careful not to be seen, it **slinked** through the leaves back to safety in a narrow gap in the rock.
2 He reminds me of my teenage son when he **slouches** off like that, back to his bed.
3 He watched it **stagger** back to the nest carrying a leaf at least ten times its size.
4 She is hard to spot as she **prowls** through the jungle, searching for her prey, which may be deer, pigs or even farm animals.
5 It **scuttled** sideways back into its hole in the sand.
6 She watched it as it patiently **stalked** a bird in the garden.
7 The huge animal **lumbered** back into the water to cool down.
8 The male tries to impress the female, circling her and **waggling** his tail.
9 There were so many of them **lurking** at the back of the toilet, it was disgusting!
10 These animals **roam** over great distances while foraging for the large quantities of food that they require to sustain their massive bodies.
11 Now they must **waddle** the eight miles back to the ocean in search of food.

12 When the rains have finished, it **burrows** back down into the earth to hibernate again.

13 They waited patiently in the car while the animals **ambled** across the road.

2 Match each verb in bold in the sentences in exercise 1 to its definition (a–m).

a) walk with short steps that make your body move from side to side

b) walk slowly because of being large and heavy

c) walk in an uncontrolled way, as if you are going to fall over

d) wait in hiding, in order to frighten, annoy or attack someone

e) sit, walk or stand with your shoulders bent forwards and your head low so that you look lazy

f) run somewhere with short quick steps

g) make something move up and down or from side to side with short, quick movements

h) move or travel in no particular direction, especially over a large area

i) move around an area in a quiet way, especially because you intend to do something bad

j) make a hole or tunnel in the ground

k) hunt a person or animal by following them without being seen

l) walk in a slow relaxed way

m) go somewhere slowly and quietly so that you will not be noticed

Animals in the story: insects

3 Here are some of the insects that appear in the extract. Look them up online or you may want to use a bilingual dictionary to give you an exact translation.

| beetle | cicada | earwig | greenfly | |
| hawk moth | hornet | lacewing fly | ladybird | |

4 Which of the insects in exercise 3:
  a) can fly?
  b) make a noise?
  c) have distinctive markings?

Animals in the story: parts of animals' bodies

5 Read the definitions and draw pictures to illustrate their meaning.

abdomen one of the three main body parts (head, thorax and abdomen) of an insect

antenna one of the two long thin parts on an insect's head that it uses to smell things with. The plural is **antennae**.

horns the hard pointed parts that usually grow in a pair on the heads of some animals, for example cows or goats

pincers the large strong parts on some insects that move like scissors, used for holding things and attacking enemies

proboscis a long tube that some insects use for feeding or sucking

stump the remaining part of an arm, leg, or tail, etc after the rest is cut off

udders the part under the body of a cow in which milk is produced

Words to describe colour and visual effect

The creatures that Gerald discovers are described in great detail, and their beauty is conveyed in the language used.

6 Read the definitions in the box. Which convey a sense of colour (C)? Which convey a sense of the quality of the light (Q)? Which combine a sense of colour with the quality of the light (CQ)?

burnished like metal that has been rubbed until it shines

chestnut red-brown

iridescent showing changing colours in different types of light

lavender light purple

luminous very bright

opal like a smooth stone used in jewellery. Opals look white like milk, but you can see other colours in them as they reflect light

pearly pale, white, or shiny like a pearl in appearance

shimmer reflect a gentle light that seems to shake slightly

translucent clear enough for light to pass through but not completely clear

Words to describe sound

7 Read the definitions and decide whether you think the words describe sounds which are:
   a) pleasant to hear?
   b) unpleasant to hear?

babble the noise of a lot of voices all talking at the same time
bleat to make the sound that a sheep or goat makes
discordant discordant music sounds strange because it contains notes that do not go together
halting with a lot of pauses between words, often because of a lack of confidence
lilting forming a gentle rising and falling pattern of sounds
melancholy making you feel sad
nasal someone with a nasal voice sounds as if they are speaking through their nose
rousing making you feel emotional, excited, or enthusiastic
shrill a shrill noise or voice is very loud and high
squawk when a bird such as a parrot squawks, it makes a loud noise in its throat

8 Complete the sentences (1–10) using the words in bold in exercise 7.

1 His voice was low and ...., as if he had a heavy cold.
2 In the distance they could hear the quiet, ... sound of a voice singing sad songs to the accompaniment of a guitar.
3 She spoke with a light, ... accent, almost as if she was singing.
4 He stumbled over his words and spoke in a ...., timid way, as if he was afraid of us.
5 A terrible .... came from the bird cage in the corner of the room and we all turned round to look.
6 As we got closer to the square the .... of voices got louder and louder as the crowd got thicker.
7 The goatherd came walking over the hill and his herd followed, ... noisily behind him.
8 The music from the band was loud and ...., making us all stand up straight and walk in time as we marched down the street.
9 From the house next door I could hear the .... sounds of a young child practising the violin.
10 The parrot froze at the sight of the child looking at it through the cage and then gave a .... cry.

Describing poor conditions

The local community around where the Durrells live is poor and many of the descriptions involve old things that are no longer in a good state. Many of the characters have a very untidy appearance.

9 **Read the sentences (1–9). Match the words in bold to their meanings (a–i).**

1 Their **tattered** clothes showed that the boys had been fighting hard.
2 The t-shirt lay **crumpled** at the bottom of a pile of clothes and needed ironing.
3 He paused to straighten his bow tie, which was **askew**.
4 The left side of his face was swollen so that the smile he gave her was **lopsided** and sad-looking.
5 She lived in a **tumbledown** cabin in the middle of the forest.
6 She wanted to use the wool from the jumper, so she started **unravelling** it.
7 I don't understand why you would buy **frayed** jeans – it looks like they're falling to pieces!
8 She wore a big **floppy** hat that fell over her eyes to protect herself from the sun.
9 After months on the streets, his beard was dirty and **shaggy**.

a) with fibres that are coming apart
b) soft and hanging down in a loose or heavy way
c) not even or level because one side is lower or bigger than the other
d) long, thick, and untidy
e) in very bad condition because parts of it have been torn, ripped or broken
f) if you do this to a piece of woollen clothing, you separated the fabric into a long thread
g) crushed like paper or cloth so that it forms untidy folds
h) at an angle instead of straight
i) a building described like this is old and in bad condition

Main themes

Before you read the extract, you may want to think about some of its main themes. The questions will help you think about the extract as you are reading it for the first time. There is more discussion of the main themes in the *Literary analysis* section after the extract.

Animals and people

The extract describes in detail many encounters that Gerald had during his time on Corfu. The animals of the garden and the surrounding landscape are an important focus in the extract, but so too are the people in his life.

10 As you read the extract, think about the animals and people:

a) What aspects of the people (his family and the friends he meets) does he describe in most detail?

b) What aspects of the animals does he focus on?

Freedom to learn

The extract tells us about a new world for the young Gerald and his freedom to explore it.

11 As you read the extract, think about the following questions:

a) What does Gerald learn? What is his attitude to the things he learns?

b) What are the circumstances that allow Gerald to follow his interests so freely?

c) What advantages does this give him? Are there any disadvantages to this kind of education?

d) If you were given the same opportunities as Gerald when you were ten, would you have spent your time doing the sorts of things that he enjoyed? Why? Why not?

My Family and Other Animals
(an extract)

by Gerald Durrell

Chapter 2
The Strawberry Pink Villa

In between keeping a watchful eye on us all, Mother was settling down in her own way. The house was redolent[1] with the scent of herbs and the sharp tang of garlic and onions, and the kitchen was full of a bubbling selection of pots, among which she moved, spectacles askew, **muttering** to herself. On the table was a **tottering** pile of books which she consulted from time to time. When she could drag herself away from the kitchen, she would drift happily about the garden, reluctantly **pruning** and cutting, enthusiastically **weeding** and planting.

For myself, the garden held sufficient interest; together Roger and I learnt some surprising things. Roger, for example, found it was unwise to smell hornets, that the peasant[2] dogs ran screaming if he glanced at them through the gate, and that the chickens that leapt suddenly from the fuchsia[3] **hedge**, squawking wildly as they fled, were unlawful prey, however desirable.

This doll's-house garden was a magic land, a forest of flowers through which roamed creatures I had never seen before. Among the thick, silky petals of each rose-bloom[4] lived tiny, crab-like spiders that scuttled sideways when disturbed. Their small, translucent bodies were coloured to match the flowers they inhabited: pink, ivory, wine-red, or buttery-yellow. On

1 *literary*: smelling of something
2 relating to poor people who work on another person's farm or on their own small farm. This word is used mainly about people in poor countries or people in history
3 a small bush with pink, red, or white flowers that hang down.
4 *literary*: a flower

the rose-stems, **encrusted** with greenflies, lady-birds moved like newly painted toys; lady-birds pale red with large black spots; lady-birds apple-red with brown spots; lady-birds orange with grey-and-black freckles. Rotund and amiable, they prowled and fed among the anaemic[5] flocks of greenfly. Carpenter bees, like furry, electric-blue bears, zigzagged among the flowers, growling fatly and busily. Humming-bird hawk-moths, **sleek** and neat, whipped up and down the paths with a fussy efficiency, pausing occasionally on speed-misty wings to lower a long, slender proboscis into a bloom. Among the white **cobbles** large black ants staggered and **gesticulated** in groups round strange trophies: a dead caterpillar, a piece of rose-petal or dried grass-head fat with seeds. As an accompaniment to all this activity there came from the olive-groves outside the fuchsia hedge the incessant shimmering cries of the cicadas. If the curious, blurring heat-haze produced a sound, it would be exactly the strange, chiming cries of these insects.

At first I was so bewildered by this profusion of life on our very own doorstep that I could only move about the garden **in a daze**, watching now this creature, now that, constantly having my attention distracted by the flights of brilliant butterflies that drifted over the hedge. Gradually, as I became more used to the bustle of insect life among the flowers, I found I could concentrate more. I would spend hours squatting on my heels or lying on my stomach watching the private lives of the creatures around me, while Roger sat nearby, a look of resignation on his face. In this way I learnt a lot of fascinating things.

I found that the little crab-spiders could change colour just as successfully as any chameleon. Take a spider from a wine-red rose, where he had been sitting like a bead of coral, and place him in the depths of a cool white rose. If he stayed there – and most of them did – you would see his colour gradually ebb away[6], as though the change had given him anaemia, until, some two days later, he would be crouching among the white petals like a pearl.

5   weak or not effective. Anaemia is a medical condition that makes you look pale and
     colourless.
6   *literary:* to gradually become smaller or less

I discovered that in the dry leaves under the fuchsia hedge lived another type of spider, a fierce little huntsman with the cunning and ferocity of a tiger. He would stalk about his continent of leaves, eyes glistening in the sun, pausing now and then to raise himself up on his hairy legs to peer about. If he saw a fly settle to enjoy a sun-bath he would freeze; then, as slowly as a leaf growing, he would move forward, imperceptibly, edging nearer and nearer, pausing occasionally to fasten his life-line of silk to the surface of the leaves. Then, when close enough, the huntsman would pause, his legs shift minutely as he **got a good purchase**, and then he would leap, legs spread out in a hairy embrace, straight on to the dreaming fly. Never did I see one of these little spiders miss its kill, once it had manoeuvred into the right position.

All these discoveries filled me with a tremendous delight so that they had to be shared, and I would burst suddenly into the house and startle the family with the news that the strange, spiky black caterpillars on the roses were not caterpillars at all, but the young of lady-birds, or with the equally astonishing news that lacewing-flies laid eggs on **stilts**. This last miracle I was lucky enough to witness. I found a lacewing-fly on the roses and watched her as she climbed about the leaves, admiring her beautiful, fragile wings like green glass, and her enormous liquid golden eyes. Presently she stopped on the surface of a rose-leaf and lowered the tip of her abdomen. She remained like that for a moment and then raised her tail, and from it, to my astonishment, rose a slender thread, like a pale hair. Then, on the very tip of this stalk, appeared the egg. The female had a rest, and then repeated the performance until the surface of the rose-leaf looked as though it was covered with a forest of tiny club moss. The laying over, the female rippled her antennae briefly and flew off in a mist of green gauze wings.

Perhaps the most exciting discovery I made in this multi-coloured Lilliput[7] to which I had access was an earwig's nest.

7 Lilliput is an imaginary place in the book *Gulliver's Travels* by Jonathan Swift, where a race of very small people live.

I had long wanted to find one and had searched everywhere without success, so the joy of **stumbling upon** one unexpectedly was overwhelming, like suddenly being given a wonderful present. I moved a piece of **bark** and there beneath it was the nursery, a small hollow in the earth that the insect must have burrowed out for herself. She squatted in the middle of it, shielding underneath her a few white eggs. She crouched over them like a hen, and did not move when the flood of sunlight struck her as I lifted the bark. I could not count the eggs, but there did not seem to be many, so I presumed that she had not yet laid her full complement. Tenderly I replaced her lid of bark.

From that moment I guarded the nest jealously. I erected a protecting wall of rocks round it, and as an additional precaution I wrote out a notice in red ink and stuck it on a pole nearby as a warning to the family. The notice read: 'BEWAR – EARWIG NEST – QUIAT PLESE.' It was only remarkable in that the two correctly spelt words were biological ones. Every hour or so I would subject the mother earwig to ten minutes' close **scrutiny**. I did not dare examine her more often for fear she might desert her nest. Eventually the pile of eggs beneath her grew, and she seemed to have become accustomed to my lifting off her bark roof. I even decided that she had begun to recognize me, from the friendly way she waggled her antennae.

To my acute disappointment, after all my efforts and constant **sentry** duty, the babies hatched out during the night. I felt that, after all I had done, the female might have held up the hatching until I was there to witness it. However, there they were, a fine **brood** of young earwigs, minute, frail, looking as though they had been carved out of **ivory**. They moved gently under their mother's body, walking between her legs, the more venturesome[8] even climbing on to her pincers. It was a heart-warming sight. The next day the nursery was empty: my wonderful family had scattered over the garden. I saw one of the babies some time later: he was bigger, of course, browner and stronger, but I recognized him immediately. He was curled up

---

8 *formal*: adventurous, willing to take risks

in a maze of rose-petals, having a sleep, and when I disturbed him he merely raised his pincers irritably over his back. I would have liked to think that it was a salute, a cheerful greeting, but honesty compelled me to admit that it was nothing more than an earwig's warning to a potential enemy. Still, I excused him. After all he had been very young when I last saw him.

I came to know the plump peasant girls who passed the garden every morning and evening. Riding side-saddle on their slouching, drooping-eared donkeys, they were shrill and colourful as parrots, and their chatter and laughter echoed among the olive-trees. In the mornings they would smile and shout greetings as their donkeys pattered past, and in the evenings they would lean over the fuchsia hedge, balancing **precariously** on their steeds'[9] backs, and smiling, hold out gifts for me – a bunch of amber grapes still sun-warmed, some figs black as **tar** striped with pink where they had **burst their seams** with ripeness, or a giant water-melon with an inside like pink ice. As the days passed, I came gradually to understand them. What had at first been a confused babble became a series of recognizable separate sounds. Then, suddenly, these took on meaning, and slowly and haltingly I started to use them myself; then I took my newly acquired words and strung them into ungrammatical and **stumbling** sentences. Our neighbours were delighted, as though I had conferred[10] some delicate compliment by trying to learn their language. They would lean over the hedge, their faces **screwed up** with concentration, as I groped my way through a greeting or a simple remark, and when I had successfully concluded they would **beam** at me, nodding and smiling and clap their hands. **By degrees** I learnt their names, who was related to whom, which were married and which hoped to be, and other details. I learnt where their little cottages were among the olive-groves, and should Roger and I chance to pass that way the entire family, vociferous[11] and pleased, would **tumble**

---

9 *literary*: a horse being ridden or that someone rides
10 *formal*: to give something, such as authority, a legal right, or an honour to someone
11 *formal*: someone who is vociferous expresses their opinion loudly and with force

out to greet us, to bring a chair, so that I might sit under their vine[12] and eat some fruit with them.

Gradually the magic of the island settled over us as gently and **clingingly** as **pollen**. Each day had a tranquility, a timelessness, about it, so that you wished it would never end. But then the dark skin of night would **peel off** and there would be a fresh day waiting for us, glossy and colourful as a child's transfer and with the same **tinge** of unreality.

Chapter 3
The Rose-beetle Man

In the morning, when I woke, the bedroom shutters were luminous and barred with gold from the rising sun. The morning air was full of the scent of **charcoal** from the kitchen fire, full of eager cock-crows[13], the distant yap of dogs, and the unsteady melancholy tune of the goat-bells as the flocks were driven out to pasture[14].

We ate breakfast out in the garden, under the small tangerine-trees. The sky was fresh and shining, not yet the fierce blue of noon, but a clear milky opal. The flowers were half-asleep, roses dew-crumpled, marigolds[15] still tightly shut. Breakfast was, on the whole, a leisurely and silent meal, for no member of the family was very talkative at that hour. By the end of the meal the influence of the coffee, toast, and eggs made itself felt, and we started to revive, to tell each other what we intended to do, why we intended to do it, and then argue earnestly as to whether each had made a wise decision. I never joined in these discussions, for I knew perfectly well what I intended to do, and would concentrate on finishing my food as rapidly as possible.

'*Must* you gulp and slush your food like that?' Larry would inquire in a pained voice, delicately picking his teeth with a match-stick.

12 a plant that grapes grow on
13 the noise the adult male chicken makes in the morning
14 *agriculture*: if you put an animal out to pasture, you put it in a field so that it can eat the grass
15 a plant which usually has bright yellow or orange flowers

'Eat it slowly, dear,' Mother would murmur; 'there's no hurry.'

No hurry? With Roger waiting at the garden gate, an alert black shape, watching for me with eager brown eyes? No hurry, with the first sleepy cicadas starting to fiddle[16] experimentally among the olives? No hurry, with the island waiting, morning cool, bright as a star, to be explored? I could hardly expect the family to understand this point of view, however, so I would slow down until I felt that their attention had been attracted elsewhere, and then stuff my mouth again.

Finishing at last, I would slip from the table and saunter towards the gate, where Roger sat gazing at me with a questioning air. Together we would peer through the wrought-iron gates into the olive-groves beyond. I would suggest to Roger that perhaps it wasn't worth going out today. He would **wag** his stump in hasty denial, and his nose would butt at my hand. No, I would say, I really didn't think we ought to go out. It looked as though it was going to rain, and I would peer up into the clear, burnished sky with a worried expression. Roger, ears cocked, would peer into the sky too, and then look at me **imploringly**. Anyway, I would go on, if it didn't look like rain now it was almost certain to rain later, and so it would be much safer just to sit in the garden with a book. Roger, in desperation, would place a large black paw on the gate, and then look at me, lifting one side of his upper lip, displaying his white teeth in a lop-sided, **ingratiating** grin, his stump working itself into a blur of excitement. This was his trump card[17], for he knew I could never resist his ridiculous grin. So I would stop teasing him, fetch my match-boxes and my butterfly net, the garden gate would creak open and clang shut, and Roger would be off through the olive-groves swiftly as a cloud-shadow, his deep bark welcoming the new day.

In those early days of exploration Roger was my constant companion. Together we ventured farther and farther afield, discovering quiet, remote olive-groves which had to be investigated and remembered, working our way through a maze

16 *informal*: to play a tune on the violin
17 an advantage you have that an opponent does not have that makes it possible for you to win

of blackbird-haunted myrtles[18], venturing into narrow valleys where the cypress-trees[19] cast a cloak[20] of mysterious, inky shadow. He was the perfect companion for an adventure, affectionate without **exuberance**, brave without being belligerent, intelligent, and full of good-humoured tolerance for my **eccentricities**. If I slipped when climbing a dew-shiny bank, Roger appeared suddenly, gave a snort that sounded like suppressed laughter, a quick look over, a rapid lick of **commiseration**, shook himself, sneezed and gave me his lop-sided grin. If I found something that interested me – an ant's nest, a caterpillar on a leaf, a spider wrapping up a fly in swaddling clothes[21] of silk – Roger sat down and waited until I had finished examining it. If he thought I was taking too long, he shifted nearer, gave a gentle, whiny yawn, and then sighed deeply and started to wag his tail. If the matter was of no great importance, we would move on, but if it was something absorbing that had to be **pored over**, I had only to frown at Roger and he would realize it was going to be a long job. His ears would droop, his tail slow down and stop, and he would slouch off to the nearest bush, and **fling** himself down in the shade, giving me a **martyred look** as he did so.

During these trips Roger and I came to know and be known by a great number of people in various parts of the surrounding countryside. There was, for example, a strange, mentally defective[22] youth with a round face as expressionless as a puffball[23]. He was always dressed in tattered shirt, shiny blue **serge** trousers that were rolled up to the knee, and on his head the elderly remains of a bowler hat[24] without a **brim**. Whenever he saw us he came hurrying through the olives, raised his absurd hat politely, and wished us good day in a voice as childish and sweet as a flute. He would stand, watching us without expression,

18 a plant with shiny leaves, white flowers, and dark purple fruit
19 a tall tree with dark green leaves that do not fall off in winter
20 *literary*: if something casts a cloak it makes a shadow appear in a particular place
21 cloth that people used in the past for wrapping babies in
22 *old-fashioned*: offensive word for someone who has learning difficulties
23 a round brown fungus that lets out seeds through an opening in its top
24 a hard round black hat, worn especially by businessmen in the past

nodding at any remark I happened to make, for ten minutes or so. Then, raising his hat politely, he would go off through the trees. Then there was the immensely fat and cheerful Agathi, who lived in a tiny tumbledown cottage high up the hill. She was always sitting outside her house with a spindle of sheep's wool, twining and pulling it into coarse thread[25]. She must have been well over seventy, but her hair was still black and lustrous, plaited carefully and wound round a pair of polished cow's horns, an ornament that some of the older peasant women adopted. As she sat in the sun, like a great black toad with a scarlet head-dress draped over the cow's horns, the bobbin of wool would rise and fall, twisting like a top, her fingers busy unravelling and plucking, and her drooping mouth with its hedge of broken and discoloured teeth wide open as she sang, loudly and harshly, but with great vigour.

It was from Agathi that I learnt some of the most beautiful and haunting of the peasant songs. Sitting on an old tin in the sun, eating grapes or pomegranates from her garden, I would sing with her, and she would **break off** now and then to correct my pronunciation. We sang (verse by verse) the gay[26], rousing song of the river, *Vangelió*, and of how it dropped from the mountains, making the gardens rich, the fields fertile, and the trees heavy with fruit. We sang, rolling our eyes at each other in exaggerated coquetry[27], the funny little love-song called 'Falsehood'. 'Lies, lies,' we warbled, shaking our heads, 'all lies, but it is my fault for teaching you to go round the countryside telling people I love you.' Then we would strike a mournful note and sing, perhaps, the slow, lilting song called 'Why are you leaving me?' We were almost overcome by this one, and would wail out the long, soulful lyrics, our voices quavering. When we came to the last bit, the most **heartrending** of all, Agathi would clasp her hands to her great breasts, her black eyes would become misty and sad, and her chins would tremble with emotion. As the last

25 Agathi is making thread from wool. *Spindle*, *twine* and *bobbin* are specialized words for this activity.
26 *old-fashioned*: happy and exciting
27 *formal*: flirtatious behaviour that is intended to attract men

discordant notes of our duet[28] faded away, she would turn to me, wiping her nose on the corner of her head-dress.

'What fools we are, eh? What fools, sitting here in the sun, singing. And of love, too! I am too old for it and you are too young, and yet we waste our time singing about it. Ah, well, let's have a glass of wine, eh?'

Apart from Agathi, the person I liked best was the old shepherd Yani, a tall, slouching man with a great hooked nose like an eagle, and incredible moustaches. I first met him one hot afternoon when Roger and I had spent an exhausting hour trying to dig a large green lizard out of its hole in a stone wall. At length, unsuccessful, sweaty, and tired, we had flung ourselves down beneath five little cypress-trees that cast a neat square of shadow on the sun-bleached grass. Lying there, I heard the gentle, drowsy tinkling of a goat-bell, and presently the herds wandered past us, pausing to stare with vacant yellow eyes, bleat **sneeringly**, and then move on. The soft sound of the bells, and of their mouths ripping and tearing at the undergrowth, had a soothing effect on me, and by the time they had drifted slowly past and the shepherd appeared I was nearly asleep. He stopped and looked at me, leaning heavily on his brown olive-wood stick, his little black eyes fierce under his shaggy brows, his big boots planted firmly in the heather.

'Good afternoon,' he greeted me **gruffly**; 'you are the foreigner … the little English lord?'

By then I was used to the curious peasant idea that all English people were lords, and I admitted that that's who I was. He turned and roared at a goat which had reared on to its hind legs and was tearing at a young olive, and then turned back.

'I will tell you something, little lord' he said; 'it is dangerous for you to lie here, beneath these trees.'

I glanced up at the cypresses, but they seemed safe enough to me, and so I asked why he thought they were dangerous.

28 *music*: a piece of music sung or played by two people

'Ah, you may *sit* under them, yes. They cast a good shadow, cold as well-water; but that's the trouble, they tempt you to sleep. And you must never, for any reason, sleep beneath a cypress.'

He paused, stroked his moustache, waited for me to ask why, and then went on:

'Why? Why? Because if you did you would be changed when you woke. Yes, the black cypresses, they are dangerous. While you sleep, their roots grow into your brains and steal them, and when you wake up you are mad, head as empty as a whistle.'

I asked whether it was only the cypress that could do this, or did it apply to other trees.

'No, only the cypress,' said the old man, peering up fiercely at the trees above me as though to see whether they were listening; 'only the cypress is the thief of intelligence. So be warned, little lord, and don't sleep here.'

He nodded briefly, gave another fierce glance at the dark blades of the cypress, as if daring them to make some comment, and then picked his way carefully through the myrtle-bushes to where his goats grazed scattered about the hill, their great udders swinging like bagpipes[29] beneath their bellies.

I got to know Yani very well, for I was always meeting him during my explorations, and occasionally I visited him in his little house, when he would **ply** me **with** fruit, and give me advice and warnings to keep me safe on my walks.

Perhaps one of the most weird and fascinating characters I met during my travels was the Rose-beetle Man. He had a fairy-tale air about him that was impossible to resist, and I used to look forward eagerly to my infrequent meetings with him. I first saw him on a high, lonely road leading to one of the remote mountain villages. I could hear him long before I could see him, for he was playing a rippling tune on a shepherd's pipe, breaking off now and then to sing a few words in a curious, nasal voice. As he rounded the corner both Roger and I stopped and stared at him in amazement.

29 *music*: a musical instrument from Scotland and Ireland, consisting of a bag with several pipes sticking out of it

He had a sharp, fox-like face with large, slanting eyes of such a dark brown that they appeared black. They had a weird, vacant look about them, and a sort of bloom[30] such as one finds on a plum, a pearly covering almost like a cataract[31]. He was short and slight, with a thinness about his wrists and neck that argued[32] a lack of food. His dress was fantastic, and on his head was a shapeless hat with a very wide, floppy brim. It had once been bottle-green, but was now speckled and smeared with dust, wine-stains and cigarette-burns. In the band were stuck a fluttering forest of feathers: cock-feathers, hoopoe-feathers, owl-feathers, the wing of a kingfisher, the claw of a hawk, and a large dirty white feather that may have come from a swan. His shirt was worn and frayed, grey with sweat, and round the neck dangled an enormous **cravat** of the most startling blue satin. His coat was dark and shapeless, with patches of different **hues** here and there; on the sleeve a bit of white cloth with a design of rosebuds; on the shoulder a triangular patch of wine-red and white spots. The pockets of this garment **bulged**, the contents almost spilling out: combs, balloons, little highly coloured pictures of the saints, olive-wood carvings of snakes, camels, dogs and horses, cheap mirrors, a riot of handkerchiefs, and long twisted rolls of bread decorated with seeds. His trousers, patched like his coat, drooped over a pair of scarlet *charouhias*, leather shoes with upturned toes decorated with a large black-and-white **pompon**. This extraordinary character carried on his back bamboo cages full of pigeons and young chickens, several mysterious sacks, and a large bunch of fresh green leeks. With one hand he held his pipe to his mouth, and in the other a number of lengths of cotton, to each of which was tied an almond-size rose-beetle, glittering golden green in the sun, all of them flying round his hat with desperate, deep buzzing, trying to escape from the thread tied firmly round their waists. Occasionally, tired of circling round and round without success,

30 *scientific:* a very thin white layer that forms on the surface of some fruits and plants
31 *medical:* a medical condition affecting your eyes in which they become white and you gradually lose the ability to see
32 *legal:* give reasons or evidence that support an idea

one of the beetles would settle for a moment on his hat, before launching itself off once more on its endless **merry-go-round**.

When he saw us the Rose-beetle Man stopped, gave a very exaggerated start, doffed his ridiculous hat[33], and swept us a low bow. Roger was so overcome by this unlooked-for attention that he let out a volley of surprised barks. The man smiled at us, put on his hat again, raised his hands, and waggled his long, bony fingers at me. Amused and rather startled by this apparition, I politely bade him good day[34]. I asked him if he had been to some fiesta. He nodded his head vigorously, raised his pipe to his lips and played a lilting little tune on it, pranced a few steps in the dust of the road, and then stopped and jerked his thumb over his shoulder, pointing back the way he had come. He smiled, patted his pockets and rubbed his forefinger and thumb together in the Greek way of expressing money. I suddenly realized that he must be dumb[35]. So, standing in the middle of the road, I carried on a conversation with him and he replied with a varied and very clever **pantomime**. I asked what the rose-beetles were for, and why he had them tied with pieces of cotton. He held his hand out to denote[36] small boys, took one of the lengths of cotton from which a beetle hung, and whirled it rapidly round his head. Immediately the insect came to life and started on its planet-like circling of his hat, and he beamed at me. Pointing up at the sky, he stretched his arms out and gave a deep nasal buzzing, while he banked and swooped across the road. Aeroplane, any fool could see that. Then he pointed to the beetles, held out his hand to denote children, and whirled his stock of beetles round his head so that they all started to buzz **peevishly**.

Exhausted by his explanation, he sat down by the edge of the road, played a short tune on his flute, breaking off to sing in his curious nasal voice. They were not **articulate** words he used, but a series of strange grunting and tenor[37] squeaks, that

33 *literary*: if you doff your hat, you take it off briefly as a greeting

34 *old-fashioned, formal*: say hello

35 *old-fashioned*: permanently unable to speak. This word is now usually considered offensive. The more usual expression is 'speech impaired'.

36 *formal*: to mean or indicate something

37 *music*: the middle and higher range of musical notes written for men to sing

appeared to be formed at the back of his throat and expelled through his nose. He produced them, however, with such **verve** and such wonderful facial expressions that you were convinced the curious sounds really meant something. Presently he stuffed his flute into his bulging pocket, gazed at me reflectively for a moment and then swung a small sack off his shoulder, undid it, and, to my delight and astonishment, tumbled half a dozen tortoises into the dusty road. Their shells had been polished with oil until they shone, and by some means or other he had managed to decorate their front legs with little red bows. Slowly and ponderously[38] they unpacked their heads and legs from their gleaming shells and set off down the road, **doggedly** and without enthusiasm. I watched them, fascinated; the one that particularly **took my fancy** was quite a small one with a shell about the size of a teacup. It seemed more **sprightly** than the others, and its shell was a paler colour – chestnut, caramel, and amber. Its eyes were bright and its walk was as alert as any tortoise's could be. I sat **contemplating** it for a long time. I convinced myself that the family would greet its arrival at the villa with tremendous enthusiasm, even, perhaps, congratulating me on finding such an elegant specimen. The fact that I had no money on me did not worry me in the slightest, for I would simply tell the man to call at the villa for payment the next day. It never occurred to me that he might not trust me. The fact that I was English was sufficient, for the islanders had a love and respect for the Englishman out of all proportion to his worth. They would trust an Englishman where they would not trust each other. I asked the Rose-beetle Man the price of the little tortoise. He held up both hands, fingers spread out. However, I hadn't watched the peasants transacting business for nothing. I shook my head firmly and held up two fingers, unconsciously imitating the man. He closed his eyes in horror at the thought, and held up nine fingers; I held up three; he shook his head, and after some thought held up six fingers; I, in return, shook my head and held up five. The Rose-beetle Man shook his head, and sighed deeply

38 moving slowly because of being big and heavy

and sorrowfully, so we sat in silence and stared at the tortoises crawling heavily and uncertainly about the road, with the curious graceless determination of babies. Presently the Rose-beetle Man indicated the little tortoise and held up six fingers again. I shook my head and held up five. Roger yawned loudly; he was thoroughly bored by this silent bargaining. The Rose-beetle Man picked up the reptile and showed me in pantomime how smooth and lovely its shell was, how erect its head, how pointed its nails. I remained **implacable**. He shrugged, handed me the tortoise, and held up five fingers.

Then I told him I had no money, and that he would have to come the next day to the villa, and he nodded as if it were the most natural thing in the world. Excited by owning this new pet, I wanted to get back home as quickly as possible in order to show it to everyone, so I said goodbye, thanked him, and hurried off along the road. When I reached the place where I had to cut down through the olive-groves, I stopped and examined my acquisition carefully. He was undoubtedly the finest tortoise I had ever seen, and worth, in my opinion, at least twice what I had paid for him. I patted his scaly head with my finger and placed him carefully in my pocket. Before diving down the hillside I glanced back. The Rose-beetle Man was still in the same place on the road, but he was doing a little **jig**, prancing and swaying, his flute warbling, while in the road at his feet the tortoises ambled to and fro, dimly and heavily.

The new arrival was duly[39] christened Achilles, and turned out to be a most intelligent and lovable beast, possessed of a peculiar sense of humour. At first he was tethered by a leg in the garden, but as he grew tamer we let him go where he pleased. He learned his name in a very short time, and we had only to call out once or twice and then wait patiently for a while and he would appear, lumbering along the narrow cobbled paths on tip-toe, his head and neck stretched out eagerly. He loved being fed, and would squat **regally** in the sun while we held out bits

39 *formal*: at the correct time

of lettuce, dandelions[40], or grapes for him. He loved grapes as much as Roger did, so there was always great **rivalry**. Achilles would sit mumbling the grapes in his mouth, the juice running down his chin, and Roger would lie nearby, watching him with agonized eyes, his mouth **drooling** saliva. Roger always had his fair share of the fruit, but even so he seemed to think it a waste to give such **delicacies** to a tortoise. When the feeding was over, if I didn't keep an eye on him, Roger would creep up to Achilles and lick his front vigorously in an attempt to get the grape-juice that the reptile had dribbled down himself. Achilles, **affronted** at such a liberty, would snap at Roger's nose, and then, when the licks became too overpowering and moist, he would retreat into his shell with an indignant wheeze, and refuse to come out until we had removed Roger from the scene.

But the fruit that Achilles liked best were the wild strawberries. He would become positively hysterical at the mere sight of them, lumbering to and fro, craning his head to see if you were going to give him any, gazing at you **pleadingly** with his tiny boot-button eyes. The very small strawberries he could devour at a gulp, for they were only the size of a fat pea. But if you gave him a big one, say the size of a hazel nut, he behaved in a way that I have never seen another tortoise emulate. He would grab the fruit and, holding it firmly in his mouth, would stumble off at top speed until he reached a safe and **secluded** spot among the flower-beds, where he would drop the fruit and then eat it at leisure, returning for another one when he had finished.

As well as developing a passion for strawberries, Achilles also developed a passion for human company. Let anyone come into the garden to sit and sun-bathe, to read or for any other reason, and before long there would be a **rustling** among the sweet williams, and Achilles' wrinkled and earnest face would be poked through. If you were sitting in a chair, he contented himself with getting as close to your feet as possible, and there he would sink into a deep and peaceful sleep, his head drooping out of his shell, his nose resting on the ground. If, however, you

40 wild plants with large yellow flowers

were lying on a rug, sun-bathing, Achilles would be convinced that you were lying on the ground simply in order to provide him with amusement. He would **surge** down the path and on to the rug with an expression of **bemused** good humour on his face. He would pause, survey you thoughtfully, and then choose a portion of your anatomy on which to practise mountaineering. Suddenly to have the sharp claws of a determined tortoise embedded in your thigh as he tries to lever himself up on to your stomach is not **conducive** to relaxation. If you shook him off and moved the rug it would only give you temporary respite[41], for Achilles would circle the garden grimly until he found you again. This habit became so tiresome that, after many complaints and threats from the family, I had to lock him up whenever we lay in the garden. Then one day the garden gate was left open and Achilles was nowhere to be found. Search-parties were immediately organized, and the family, who up till then had spent most of their time openly making threats against the reptile's life, wandered about the olive-groves, shouting, 'Achilles ... strawberries, Achilles ... Achilles ... strawberries ...' At length we found him. Ambling along in his usual detached manner, he had fallen into a disused well, the wall of which had long since disintegrated, and the mouth of which was almost covered in ferns. He was, to our regret, quite dead. Even Leslie's attempts at artificial respiration, and Margo's suggestion of forcing strawberries down his throat (to give him, she explained, something to live for), failed to get any response. So, mournfully and solemnly, his corpse was buried in the garden under a small strawberry plant (Mother's suggestion). A short funeral address, written and read in a trembling voice by Larry, made the occasion a memorable one. It was only **marred** by Roger, who, in spite of all my protests, insisted on wagging his tail throughout the burial service.

Not long after Achilles had been taken from us I obtained another pet from the Rose-beetle Man. This time it was a pigeon. He was still very young and had to be force-fed on bread-and-

41 *formal*: a short period of rest from having to deal with a difficult or unpleasant situation

milk and soaked corn. He was the most revolting bird to look at, with his feathers pushing through the wrinkled scarlet skin, mixed with the horrible yellow down that covers baby pigeons and makes them look as though they have been **peroxiding** their hair. Owing to his repulsive and **obese** appearance, Larry suggested we call him Quasimodo[42] and, liking the name without realizing the implications, I agreed. For a long time after he could feed himself, and when all his feathers had grown, Quasimodo retained a sprig of yellow down on his head which gave him the appearance of a rather pompous judge wearing a wig several sizes too small.

Owing to his **unorthodox** upbringing and the fact that he had no parents to teach him the facts of life, Quasimodo became convinced that he was not a bird at all, and refused to fly. Instead he walked everywhere. If he wanted to get on to a table, or a chair, he stood below it, ducking his head and cooing in a rich contralto until someone lifted him up. He was always eager to join us in anything we did, and would even try to come for walks with us. This, however, we had to stop, for either you carried him on your shoulder, which was risking an accident to your clothes, or else you let him walk behind. If you let him walk, then you had to slow down your own pace to suit his, for should you get too far head you would hear the most frantic and imploring coos and turn round to find Quasimodo running desperately after you, his tail wagging seductively, his iridescent chest **pouted out** with indignation at your cruelty.

Quasimodo insisted on sleeping in the house; no amount of **coaxing** or scolding[43] would get him to inhabit the pigeon-loft I had constructed for him. He preferred to sleep on the end of Margo's bed. Eventually, however, he was banished[44] to the drawing room sofa, for if Margo turned over in bed at night Quasimodo would wake, hobble up the bed, and perch on her face, cooing loudly and lovingly.

---

42 an ugly character in the novel *The Hunchback of Notre-Dame* by Victor Hugo
43 *old-fashioned*: tell someone off, especially a child, severely and angrily for something they have done wrong
44 *often humorous*: to make someone go somewhere else

It was Larry who discovered that Quasimodo was a musical pigeon. Not only did he like music, but he actually seemed to recognize two different varieties, the waltz and the military march. For ordinary music he would waddle as close to the gramophone[45] as possible and sit there with pouting chest, eyes half closed, purring softly to himself. But if the tune was a waltz he would move round and round the machine, bowing, twisting, and cooing tremulously. For a march, on the other hand – Sousa[46] for preference – he drew himself up to his full height, inflated his chest, and stamped up and down the room, while his coo became so rich and throaty that he seemed in danger of strangling himself. He never attempted to perform these actions for any other kind of music except marches and waltzes. Occasionally, however, if he had not heard any music for some time, he would (in his enthusiasm at hearing the gramophone) do a march for a waltz, or vice versa, but he invariably stopped and corrected himself half-way through.

One sad day we found, on waking Quasimodo, that he had **duped** us all, for there among the cushions lay a glossy white egg. He never quite recovered from this. He became embittered, **sullen**, and started to peck irritably if you attempted to pick him up. Then he laid another egg, and his nature changed completely. He, or rather she, became wilder and wilder, treating us as though we were her worst enemies, slinking up to the kitchen door for food as if she feared for her life. Not even the gramophone would tempt her back into the house. The last time I saw her she was sitting in an olive-tree, cooing in the most pretentious and **coy** manner, while further along the branch a large and very masculine-looking pigeon twisted and cooed in a perfect ecstasy of admiration.

For some time the Rose-beetle Man would turn up at the villa fairly regularly with some new addition to my **menagerie**: a frog, perhaps, or a sparrow[47] with a broken leg. One afternoon Mother and I, in a fit of extravagant **sentimentalism**, bought up

45 *old-fashioned*: a piece of equipment for playing music on records
46 an American composer, known for his marches
47 a small brown bird that is common in the US and northern Europe

his entire stock of rose-beetles and, when he had left, let them all go in the garden. For days the villa was full of rose-beetles, crawling on the beds, lurking in the bathroom, banging against the lights at night, and falling like emeralds into our laps.

The last time I saw the Rose-beetle Man was one evening when I was sitting on a hill-top overlooking the road. He had obviously been to some fiesta and had been **plied with** much wine, for he swayed to and fro across the road, piping a melancholy tune on his flute. I shouted a greeting, and he waved extravagantly without looking back. As he rounded the corner he was silhouetted for a moment against the pale lavender evening sky. I could see his battered hat with the fluttering feathers, the bulging pockets of his coat, the bamboo cages full of sleepy pigeons on his back, and above his head, circling drowsily round and round, I could see the dim specks that were the rose-beetles. Then he rounded the curve of the road and there was only the pale sky with a new moon floating in it like a silver feather, and the soft twittering of his flute dying away in the dusk.

Post-reading activities

Understanding the story

Use these questions to help you check that you have understood the story.

Chapter Two

1 What does Mother spend her time doing? Does she do these things because she has to or because she wants to?

2 How does Roger learn that you shouldn't smell hornets?

3 What is Gerald's first impression of the wildlife in the garden? How does his approach to observing wildlife develop?

4 What does Gerald learn about:
   a) the crab-like spiders
   b) the huntsman spider
   c) the black caterpillars
   d) the lacewing-flies

5 Why does the discovery of the earwig nest mean so much to him?

6 Why is the incident with the earwigs humorous?

7 How do the local people make him feel welcome?

8 What is the Gerald Durrell method for learning Greek?

9 How did he feel at the end of each day? How does each new day seem?

Chapter Three

10 Why does Gerald eat breakfast so fast?

11 What game does he play with Roger before they leave?

12 What equipment does he take with him? Why?

13 What activities do both Roger and Gerald enjoy? What doesn't Roger like so much?

14 What does Gerald sing about with Agathi? Why is this inappropriate for them to do, according to her?

15 What are Gerald and Agathi like as singers?

16 What does Yani warn him against?

17 What is unusual about:
   a) the Rose-beetle Man's singing?
   b) his hat?
   c) the contents of his pockets?
   d) his shoes?
   e) what he is carrying on his back?
   f) what he is carrying in his hands?

18 What does Gerald think explains the man's appearance? Is he correct?
19 How does the Rose-beetle Man earn money?
20 Why does Gerald choose the one tortoise over the others?
21 Where did Gerald learn his money skills?
22 Why did the man trust Gerald to pay him the following day, according to Gerald?
23 How much does the Rose-beetle Man want for the tortoise? How much does he get?
24 Does Gerald regret buying the tortoise? Why? Why not?
25 What is Roger's problem with the new pet?
26 What problem do the other family members have with Achilles?
27 Do the rest of the family really dislike Achilles? How do we know?
28 How is Gerald's attitude to Quasimodo different from that of his other pets?
29 How does Quasimodo annoy people?
30 What kind of 'accident' could happen if you carried Quasimodo?
31 What is Quasimodo's unusual hobby?
32 How does Quasimodo surprise them all? Why is it a 'sad day'?

Language study

Grammar

Would for past habits

In describing Gerald's life while he lived on Corfu, the story recounts specific or special events as well as regular occurrences (things he often did).

1 Are the following extracts (a–g) describing specific events or regular occurrences? How do you know?

a) *I would spend hours squatting on my heels or lying on my stomach watching the private lives of the creatures around me.*

b) *I moved a piece of bark and there beneath it was the nursery.*

c) *In the mornings they would smile and shout greetings as their donkeys pattered past.*

d) *I never joined in these discussions.*

e) *I used to look forward eagerly to my infrequent meetings with him.*

f) *I first saw him on a high, lonely road leading to one of the remote mountain villages.*

g) *She was always sitting outside her house with a spindle of sheep's wool.*

2 Use extracts (a–g) in exercise 1 to complete the grammar rules below with one word.

We can describe past actions which happened regularly in several ways:
With the modal verb 1) ....
With an adverb of frequency, e.g. 2) ....
With the structure 3) .... *to*
With the past continuous and the adverb of frequency 4) ....

Would is used in a similar way to *used to*, to describe repeated habitual actions that happened in the past but no longer happen today. We cannot use *would* or *used to* when the specific number of times the action occurs is stated.

3 Which of these sentences is not possible?

a) I would meet him three times.
b) I used to meet him three times.
c) I met him three times.

There are some important differences between *would* and *used to*. When *would* has this past meaning, it is not normally used with stative verbs, such as *be*, *think*, *love* and *believe*, but *used to* can be used with stative verbs. Also, *used to* can describe a past action that happened only once over a long period of time, whereas *would* describes something that happened more than once.

4 Look at these extracts from the story. Which of the verbs in bold (1–3) can be replaced by *used to*? Which can be replaced by *would*?

> Agathi, who (1) **lived** in a tiny tumbledown cottage high up the hill. She (2) **was always sitting** outside her house with a spindle of sheep's wool …

> He (3) **loved** being fed.

5 The following sentences from the story all have a main clause and at least one subordinate clause, such as a time clause or a conditional clause. Underline the main clause. The first one is done for you.

a) <u>I would spend hours squatting on my heels or lying on my stomach</u> watching the private lives of the creatures around me, while Roger sat nearby.
b) I would slow down until I felt that their attention had been attracted elsewhere, and then stuff my mouth again.
c) If he saw a fly settle to enjoy a sun-bath, he would freeze.
d) As the last discordant notes of our duet faded away, she would turn to me, wiping her nose on the corner of her head-dress.

6 **In exercise 5, where does *would* appear in the sentences (a–d)? What tense(s) are the verbs in the other clauses?**

7 **In the following passage, all the verbs in bold (1–12) are in the past simple. Change them to *would* where possible, and *used to* if this is possible.**

Before I (1) **came** here, my family (2) **lived** in South Africa, and whenever I (3) **had** a school holiday, we (4) **spent** our holidays on safari because my father (5) **was** a keen photographer. I (6) **loved** those trips. We even (7) **camped** in a tree house hotel.

I (8) **spent** hours in the observation hut watching the zebra, wildebeest and impala. Sometimes, we (9) **saw** lions but they always (10) **kept** their distance. I once (11) **spotted** a white rhino; these (12) **were** very rare but numbers are slowly recovering now. I've been interested in conservation since those holidays.

Multiple-clause sentences

One of the features of an authentic text is a variety in sentence length. Some sentences in the story are very short – just a few words. They are used for several reasons. For example, they can imitate the quick-fire expressions used in speech:

No hurry?

They can be used to introduce a new theme at the beginning of sentences:

It was Larry who discovered that Quasimodo was a musical pigeon.

Or they can be used for dramatic effect:

I suddenly realized that he must be dumb.

Other sentences contain many clauses, so their structure is often very complex. They may be used to create atmosphere, describe a long complex series of actions or build up detail.

8 **Look at this example from the extract. It contains eight clauses. Can you identify them?**

He would grab the fruit and, holding it firmly in his mouth, would stumble off at top speed until he reached a safe and secluded spot among the flower-beds, where he would drop the fruit and then eat it at leisure, returning for another one when he had finished.

Look at how the clauses break down into individual single-clause sentences:

He would grab the fruit.
He would hold it firmly in his mouth.
He would stumble off at top speed.
He reached a safe and secluded spot among the flower-beds.
He would drop the fruit there.
He would eat it at leisure.
He would finish.
He would return for another one.

In this case, the long sentence helps to convey the way the complex behaviour that Achilles the tortoise shows when he is given a strawberry. Notice how commas are used to separate the various clauses and help us process the sentence as we read it.

9 Look at the extract below from the story. It contains six clauses. Rewrite it as six simple sentences using the guide below.

She must have been well over seventy, but her hair was still black and lustrous, plaited carefully and wound round a pair of polished cow's horns, an ornament that some of the older peasant women adopted.

1 She ....
2 Her hair ....
3 It was ....
4 It was ....
5 This was ....
6 Some of the ....

10 Look at another example. How many clauses are there in this sentence? Use commas to separate the clauses where necessary. Check your answers on pages 185–6.

Together we ventured farther and farther afield discovering quiet, remote olive-groves which had to be investigated and remembered, working our way through a maze of blackbird-haunted myrtles, venturing into narrow valleys where the cypress-trees cast a cloak of mysterious, inky shadow.

11 Now break the sentence down into separate sentences. Compare your sentences to the one in the story. What is the difference in the effect?

Multiple-clause sentences exist in most types of authentic text. They can be very effective but their length and complexity can also be confusing. One way to make multiple-clause sentences easier to understand is to break them down into shorter clauses as you have done here.

Literary analysis

Plot

1 List the main events in the extract. Are most of them in Chapter Two or Chapter Three? What is the main focus of the other chapter?
2 The extract comes from near the beginning of the book. We know that the Durrells lived on Corfu for four years. When do you think the events that are described here occurred? Which are early in their time on the island and which are later?
3 Read these two extracts from Chapter Two. What process do they each describe? What do these processes have in common?

  a) *At first I was so bewildered by this profusion of life … that I could only move about the garden in a daze … Gradually, as I became more used to the bustle of insect life among the flowers, I found I could concentrate more … In this way I learnt a lot of fascinating things.*

  b) *As the days passed, I came gradually to understand them. What had at first been a confused babble became a series of recognizable separate sounds. Then, suddenly, these took on meaning.*

4 Gerald learns a lot about wildlife in Corfu. What else does he learn?
5 How do you think the family react to the 'astonishing news' that, for example, lacewing-flies lay eggs on stilts?
6 How does Gerald's hobby affect the rest of his family?
7 Think about the different ways that Gerald communicates with the people he meets. Match the characters (a–d) to the best description of their relationship with him (i–iv):

  a) the youth with the bowler hat
  b) Agathi
  c) Yani
  d) the Rose-beetle Man

  i) They understand each other through signs and gestures.
  ii) They connect with each other emotionally through the shared experience of singing.
  iii) They follow the conventions of polite conversation.
  iv) One passes on knowledge to the other.

8   At the end of Chapter Two, the writer expresses the idea that each day on Corfu had a 'tinge of unreality'. What contributes to this sense of illusion?

9   Do you think that the events in the rest of the book are told chronologically (the order in which they happened) or will each chapter will take a different theme so that the plot goes back and forth in time?

10 Would you like to read the rest of the story? Why? Why not?

Character

11 Read the first paragraph of the extract again (on page 179, beginning 'In between keeping …'), which introduces Gerald's mother. What impression of her are we given? Is she described sympathetically (i.e. are we meant to care about her and like her)?

12 What kind of person is Gerald? Think about his age, his interests, his interpersonal skills, and how he compares to other children his age.

13 Why does the episode with the earwigs tell us more about Gerald than it does about the earwigs?

14 In what ways does Gerald have a freedom that children of his age usually don't have?

15 What impression are we given of the local peasants?

16 Which of the adults that we meet in this extract is Gerald most interested in? Why is this adult so interesting to him? How do we know he is interested in them?

17 Which of the Greek characters in the story treat Gerald most like an adult?

18 What can we tell about Gerald's older brothers and sister from their reaction to Achilles' death?

19 Think about the characters that you have been introduced to in this extract. Which one would you like to find out more about in the rest of the book? Why?

Animals in the story

20 The book is called My Family and Other Animals. What do you understand to be the meaning of the title?

21 What role does Roger play in Gerald's life in Corfu?

22 Why does Gerald appreciate Roger so much?

23 What human-like characteristics are ascribed to Roger?

24 Think about the insects that the story teller describes in Chapter Two. Which insect(s):
 a) work hard?
 b) is patient?
 c) is clever and fierce?
 d) are we told are friendly?
 e) are like airplanes?
 f) are compared to colourful toys?
25 Both Achilles and Quasimodo make unusual pets. What differences are there between them in terms of their position in the family?
26 Choose one of the animals that we read about in the extract. Write about its effect on Gerald: what he learns about it, what impressions he gets from it. Also say why you chose that animal.

Narration

27 How much of the extract talks about unique events compared to daily routines?
28 *My Family and Other Animals* is an autobiography, so the main character is the same as the storyteller. However, the adult writing the book is in some ways a different person from the ten-year-old in the story, and views some of the events in a different way. Read the extract below about the earwig nest. Where do we see the story teller's voice as separate from that of the young Gerald?

 The notice read: 'BEWAR – EARWIG NEST – QUIAT PLESE.' It was only remarkable in that the two correctly spelt words were biological ones…

 … raised his pincers irritably over his back. I would have liked to think that it was a salute, a cheerful greeting, but honesty compelled me to admit that it was nothing more than an earwig's warning to a potential enemy. Still, I excused him. After all he had been very young when I last saw him.

29 What effect does this separation between the story teller and the main character have?
30 How much dialogue is there in the extract? How does the amount of dialogue reflect Gerald's life?
31 Read the dialogue between Gerald and Yani on page 188 again. Look at the way that the story teller reports Yani's speech and Gerald's speech. What do you notice about Gerald's side of the conversation? What is the effect of this?

32　Even though we don't hear Gerald's voice directly, we do sometimes hear his internal voice, such as in this extract from the scene with the Rose-beetle Man:

Pointing up at the sky, he stretched his arms out and gave a deep nasal buzzing, while he banked and swooped across the road. Aeroplane, any fool could see that.

What emotion is expressed in the second sentence?

33　Look again at the breakfast scene at the beginning of Chapter Three (page 184). Where do we hear Gerald's inner voice here? What emotion does it express? Why doesn't he express his emotion to his family?

34　What do the ends of each chapter have in common? What is the effect of ending this way?

Style

Comparison: simile and metaphor

35　Gerald frequently compares things that he sees and hears to other things in order to give a clearer idea of what he experiences. He uses different techniques to do this.
Read the extracts (1–3) below from the beginning of the story and find phrases in bold that compare:
a)　colours of plants to the colours of food
b)　small animals to larger animals
c)　small places to large places
d)　the way a small animal moves to the way a plant moves
e)　the way small animals move to the way large animals move
f)　things in the natural world to artificial things.

1　**This doll's-house garden was a magic land**, *a forest of flowers through which* **roamed** *creatures I had never seen before. Among the thick, silky petals of each rose-bloom lived tiny,* **crab-like spiders** *that* **scuttled** *sideways when disturbed. Their small, translucent bodies were coloured to match the flowers they inhabited: pink, ivory,* **wine-red**, *or* **buttery-yellow**. *On the rose-stems, encrusted with greenflies, lady-birds moved* **like newly painted toys**.

2　*I found that the little crab-spiders could change colour just* **as successfully as any chameleon**. *Take a spider from a wine-red rose, where he had been sitting* **like a bead of coral**, *and place him in* **the depths of a cool white rose**.

3 *Under the fuchsia hedge lived another type of spider,* **a fierce little huntsman with the cunning and ferocity of a tiger**. *He would stalk about* **his continent of leaves**. *If he saw a fly settle to enjoy a sun-bath he would freeze; then,* **as slowly as a leaf growing**, *he would move forward, imperceptibly.*

36 What are the effects of the comparisons on the descriptions in question 35?

Two ways of comparing different things are by simile and metaphor. A simile is when you say that something is similar to another thing. For example, *crab-like spiders* means that the spiders are similar to crabs. Metaphor is when you say that something actually *is* something else. For example, *this doll's-house garden* suggests that the garden actually *is* the garden of a doll's house.

37 Look at the rest of the phrases in bold (1–3) in the extracts in question 35 again. Decide whether the comparisons are made using similes or metaphors.

38 Read the following extracts (a–d) from later in the story. Use one word to create a simile for each extract.

  a) *… some figs black ……………………… tar.*
  b) *Yani, a tall, slouching man with a great hooked nose ……………………… an eagle.*
  c) *He had a sharp, fox-……………………… face.*
  d) *… tortoises crawling about the road, with the graceless determination ……………………… babies.*

39 Read the following extract out loud. Which sound is repeated? What effect does it create?

  In the band were stuck **a fluttering forest of feathers**: *cock-feathers, hoopoe-feathers, owl-feathers, the wing of a kingfisher, the claw of a hawk, and a large dirty white feather that may have come from a swan.*

40 The extract in question 39 contains a list. Find another list in the description of the Rose-beetle Man (page 190). What is the effect of lists in the description?

Synaesthesia

Synaesthesia (pronounced /ˌsɪnɪsˈθiːziə/) is an interesting condition that affects some people and means that when one sense is stimulated, another is also stimulated. For example, some people with this condition smell different smells depending on which letter of the alphabet they are reading!

To people without synaesthesia, this mixing of the senses may seem extremely strange. However, we will be familiar with a form of synaesthesia in language. For example, we talk about 'cool colours' such as blues and greens and 'warm colours' like reds and oranges. Here, touch (temperature) and vision (colour) are mixed. A 'sharp taste' mixes touch with taste, used to describe the taste of acid.

In literature, too, writers make use of synesthetic devices to achieve certain effects.

41 In the following extract, identify three instances of synaesthesia:

Carpenter bees, like furry, electric-blue bears, zigzagged among the flowers, growling fatly and busily… As an accompaniment to all this activity there came from the olive-groves outside the fuchsia hedge the incessant shimmering cries of the cicadas. If the curious, blurring heat-haze produced a sound, it would be exactly the strange, chiming cries of these insects.

42 How does the synesthetic device reflect Gerald's experience in the garden?

43 Read the last paragraph of Chapter Two (page 184) from 'Gradually the magic …'. A comparison is made by the idea of 'clinging' and 'peeling'. What is this image? Is there anything that puts in question the positive phrase 'fresh day'?

44 How well does the ending conclude the chapter, in your opinion? Why?

45 Now read this extract from the last paragraph of Chapter Three. How well does it conclude the chapter? What images and emotions are created? How are they similar or different from the end of Chapter Two?

As he rounded the corner he was silhouetted for a moment against the pale lavender evening sky. I could see his battered hat with the fluttering feathers, the bulging pockets of his coat, the bamboo cages full of sleepy pigeons on his back, and above his head, circling drowsily round and round, I could see the dim specks that were the rose-beetles. Then he rounded the curve of the road and there was only the pale sky with a new moon floating in it like a silver feather, and the soft twittering of his flute dying away in the dusk.

Guidance to the above literary terms, answer keys to all the exercises and activities, plus a wealth of other reading-practice material, can be found at: www.macmillanenglish.com/readers.

Essay questions

Language analysis

> Discuss how one of the language areas you've studied contributes to the telling of two OR MORE of the stories in the collection.

Analysing the question

What is the question asking?

It is asking you to:
- choose one language area from the index on page 221
- explain how this language area functions in the context of storytelling in this collection
- use extracts from two or more of the stories in the collection as examples.

Preparing your answer

1 Look back through the *Language study* sections of the stories and extracts you've read and choose a language area that you feel confident about.
2 Make notes about the language area. Include notes on form, function and use.
3 Choose examples from two stories. If possible, choose extracts from different periods.
4 Look back at the question and your notes and plan your essay. Here is an example of an essay plan:

Introduction	Introduce the area you are going to describe.
Main body 1	Explain the general function of the area you have chosen. Use examples from more than one story.
Main body 2	Analyze how the area contributes to the style, narrative or atmosphere of the stories, referring to specific passages in the stories.
Conclusion	Summarize the literary use and function of the language area you focused on.

Literary analysis

Choose two stories from this collection. Compare and contrast the way that animals in the story have had an effect on the human characters. Consider the characters' attitude to the animals, any significant events, and the role of the animals in their lives and relationships.

Analysing the question
What is the question asking?

It is asking you to:
- look at two stories in the collection
- outline the personalities of the main characters and their situations
- describe the role of the animals in their lives and any impact that the animals have had on them
- describe any similarities and differences between the two stories.

Preparing your answer

1 Choose two stories that interest you and that seem particularly relevant to this question.
2 Make notes about the personality and situation of at least one human character in each story: what they are like; the lifestyle they lead; how they feel, and so on.
3 Find key scenes in the stories where they interact with at least one animal and where the animal affects them in some way. Make a note of any useful quotations.
4 Make a list of similarities and differences between the stories in regard to the animal's role in the character's life.
5 Read the question again and write a plan for your essay. Here is an example:

Introduction	Briefly introduce the two stories
Story 1	Describe the interaction between the characters and animals in the first story and their impact on the people.

Story 2	Describe the interaction between the characters and animals in the second story and their impact on the people.
Similarities	Compare the ways that the animals have affected the characters. What common points do they share?
Differences	Contrast the two stories in this regard. How do they differ?
Conclusion	Make a general comment about the significance of the animals in both stories.

Glossary

The definitions in the glossary refer to the meanings of the words and phrases as they are used in the short stories in this collection. Some words and phrases may also have other meanings that are not given here. The definitions are arranged in the story in which they appear, and in alphabetical order.

The Cat that Walked by Himself

all the same `PHRASE` despite what has been mentioned

at my wits' end `PHRASE` so worried and tired because of your problems that you cannot think of any more ways of solving them

blessing (n) permission or support for something

comfy (adj) *informal*: comfortable

footstool (n) a small, low piece of furniture for resting your feet on

for the sake of `PHRASE` for the purpose of doing, getting, or achieving something

halter (n) a thin piece of leather or rope fastened around a horse's head and used for leading the horse

hatchet (n) a tool used for cutting wood. It is similar to a small axe

head over heels `PHRASE` if you fall head over heels, you fall so that your head goes down and your feet go up in the air

knobby (adj) covered with small, hard lumps

lap (n) the top half of your legs above your knees when you sit down

lo and behold `PHRASE` *often humorous*: used for introducing something surprising that you are about to tell or show someone

mew (v) if a cat or kitten mews, it makes a short, very high sound

mutton (n) the meat from an adult sheep

new-mown (adj) new-mown grass or hay that has just been cut

pat (v) touch an animal gently with a flat hand in a friendly way

pebble (n) a small stone, especially one that has been made smooth by water

praise (n) an expression of strong approval or admiration

pussy (n) *informal*: a cat. This word is used mainly by children or when speaking to children.

The Princess and the Puma

aggrieved (adj) feeling angry and unhappy because you think you have been treated in an unfair way

air (n) an appearance or attitude that someone has

amber (n) between brown and yellow in colour

anti-climax (n) something that is not as exciting as you expected it to be so that

you feel disappointed

bungle (v) do something badly and without success

burden (n) something heavy that you have to carry

clump (n) a group of trees or plants growing very close together

fiasco (n) a complete and embarrassing failure

gaze (n) way of looking at someone or something

glare (v) look at someone or something in a very angry way

grief (n) a strong feeling of sadness, usually because someone has died

indisputable (adj) impossible to question or argue with

in token of PHRASE as sign of

intrepidity (n) from the adjective **intrepid** not afraid to do dangerous things, the adjective is more common than the noun

leased (adj) buildings, land, or equipment that are leased are rented for a specific period of time

machete (n) a large knife with a long wide blade, used as a weapon or tool

make amends PHRASE to try to make a situation better after you have done something wrong

mockery (n) behaviour intended to make someone seem stupid, for example by laughing at them

oppressive (adj) something that is oppressive makes you feel very worried or unhappy

penitently (adv) in a way that shows you feel sorry for something bad that you have done and are willing to change your behaviour

presumptuous (adj) showing too much confidence and not enough respect

prospect (v) search for gold, oil, or another valuable substance

provoking (adj) deliberately trying to make someone angry

rascal (n) *humourous*: someone who behaves badly but who you like too much to be angry with

reproach (n) an expression of criticism and disappointment because of something bad that someone has done

saccharine (n) very romantic or emotional, in a way that seems false and annoying

scarce (adj) if something is scarce, there is not very much of it

scorn (v) think something is stupid or not good enough for them

shiver (v) shake slightly

sojourner (n) traveller, from **sojourn** a period of time when you stay in a place that is not your home

strayed (adj) from the verb **stray** move away from the correct place or path

streak (n) a line or long mark on something that is a different colour from the colour surrounding it

teasing (adj) from the verb **tease** say something to someone in order to have fun by embarrassing or annoying them slightly

timber (n) wood used for building houses or making furniture, or the trees where it comes from

weave (v) make cloth by crossing long threads over and under each other on a machine called a loom

would-be (adj) (before a noun) hoping or trying to do something

wrinkled (adj) cloth or paper that is wrinkled has a lot of small accidental folds on it

The Grey Parrot

artful (adj) skilled at getting something from people, especially in a dishonest way

at no pains PHRASE making no special effort

bent on (doing) something PHRASE very determined to achieve something

bonnet (n) a hat that ties under your chin

bridegroom (n) a man who is getting married, or who has recently married

bustle (v) do something or go somewhere quickly, usually because you are very busy

charms (n) pleasant or attractive qualities or features

clasp knife (n) a knife with a blade that folds into its handle

copious (adj) *formal*: large, or in large amounts

damn it PHRASE impolite exclamation used when you are annoyed about something

deceitful (adj) behaving dishonestly in order to trick people

disposition (n) the way that someone normally thinks and behaves, that shows what type of person they are

eerie (adj) strange and mysterious, and sometimes frightening

embrace (n) *formal*: the action of putting your arms around someone to show love or friendship

en route PHRASE on the way (a French phrase that is commonly used in English)

fancy (v) *informal*: exclamation used when you are very surprised about something

for someone's sake PHRASE for the benefit or good of someone or something

fray (n) a fight or argument

furnish (v) give someone something they need, especially information

give way PHRASE agree to something that someone else wants

handkerchief (n) a small square piece of cloth or paper used for wiping your nose or eyes

heartiness (n) friendliness and enthusiasm

ill-concealed (adj) an ill-concealed feeling is one you do not hide well, so that other people can see how you feel

indignant (adj) angry because of someone's unfair or shocking behaviour

irredeemably (adv) from the adjective **irredeemable** *formal* impossible to make better

landlady (n) a woman who owns a house, flat, or room that people can rent

mischief (n) trouble or disagreement that someone deliberately causes

misgivings (n) a feeling of doubt about whether something is right or will have a good result

monotony (n) a bored feeling caused by the fact that nothing different ever happens

mope (v) feel bored or unhappy and show no interest in doing anything

nonsense (n) unreasonable or annoying behaviour

opera-glasses (n) an object that you look through so that you can see the actors on a stage more clearly

outrage (n) an event or action that makes you feel extremely angry and upset

parasol (n) a type of umbrella designed to provide protection from the sun

pitch (v) throw something using a lot of force

prophetic (adj) describing something that will happen in the future

scarlet (adj) bright red in colour

see fit PHRASE decide that something is the best thing to do

soothe (v) make someone more calm when they are feeling nervous, worried, or upset

stab (v) kill or hurt someone by pushing a knife or other sharp object into their body

stalk (v) walk in a way that shows you feel angry or offended

unconscious (adj) used about things you do without realizing you are doing them or that other people have noticed you doing them, or without intending to do them

want (n) *formal* a lack of something

waver (v) if a person wavers, they are not certain about what to say or do

with a vengeance PHRASE used for emphasizing that something happens in an extreme way

wring something's neck (past participle **wrung**) PHRASE to kill an animal by squeezing and twisting its neck

yarn (n) a long detailed excuse or explanation that is completely false

Lappin and Lapinova

bawl (v) shout loudly

be blessed with something PHRASE to have something very good or special

blister (n) a swollen area on your skin that is full of a clear liquid and is caused by something rubbing against it

blur (v) make it difficult to see something clearly

carnation (n) a flower often worn at weddings

decayed (adj) old and neglected (not looked after)

din (n) a very loud unpleasant noise that lasts for a long time

disperse (v) extend, or make things extend, in different directions over a wide area

dread (v) feel very worried about something that is going to happen

dusk (n) the period of time at the end of the day just before it becomes dark

faint (v) suddenly become unconscious for a short time, and usually fall to the ground

foible (n) a way of thinking or behaving that is unusual and strange or annoying

giddiness (n) a feeling that you might fall, similar to fainting

grimly (adv) in a very serious and unfriendly way

icicle (n) a long thin piece of ice that hangs down from somewhere

in league PHRASE secretly working with someone

inquisitive (adj) showing an interest in something, being curious

intertwined (adj) twisted together

lacy (adj) looking like lace, a light delicate cloth with patterns of small holes in it

lark (n) a small brown bird that is known for singing while it flies

mere (adj) used for emphasizing that something is small or unimportant

of its own accord PHRASE **do something of your own accord** is to do something without being asked, forced, or helped by someone else

peal out (phrasal verb) if a bell peals out, it makes a loud sound (here used to describe loud piece of music)

pitiable (adj) making you feel sympathy and sadness

ramrod (n) a long, thin stick

resplendent (adj) *literary*: impressive to look at

settled (adj) if something is settled, people have made a decision about it

sham (adj) not real but claimed to be real

slyly (adv) from the adjective **sly**, a sly smile, look, or remark shows that the person doing it knows something that other people do not know

sob (n) the noise you make when you cry noisily while taking short breaths

stealthily (adv) in a quiet and secret way so that no one sees or hears you

stiff (adj) if you are stiff, you feel pain in your muscles and cannot move easily

stubby (adj) short and thick

sumptuous (adj) impressive, expensive, and of high quality

to let PHRASE available to be rented

vivid (adj) having or producing very clear and detailed images in the mind

whimper (v) say something in a voice that expresses pain, fear, or sadness

Brown Wolf

abruptly (adv) in a sudden and unexpected way

advances (n) attempts to make friends with someone

attuned (adj) familiar with something and able to deal with it in a sensitive way

awe (v) create respect, admiration, and sometimes fear in other people

belligerent (adj) very unfriendly and angry

circumspect (adj) slow and careful

clattering (n) the sound of a hard object as it hits against another hard object or surface

clinch (v) do one last thing that makes success certain

cool and collected PHRASE calm and able to control your feelings

dent (v) push the surface of something inwards

dingy (adj) dark and dirty-looking

droop (v) hang downwards

drowsy (adj) feeling that you want to sleep

extravagance (n) way of speaking that uses too many complicated and poetic words

fastidiously (adv) very carefully, fussily

flee (v) (past tense **fled**) escape

flounder (v) feel confused and lost and not know what to say or do next

flush (v) if someone flushes, their face becomes red

flutter (v) with short, quick, light movements

futility (n) a lack of purpose, importance, or effectiveness

gem (n) a precious stone, here it is used figuratively to describe Walt's poems

give the lie to something PHRASE to show that something is not true

glide (v) move in a smooth and easy way with no noise

gurgling (adj) making the low sound of moving water

haunches (n) the upper part of an animal's or human's legs and hips

homing instinct (n) if an animal or bird has a homing instinct, it is able to find its way home across long distances

jerk (n) a quick, sudden movement

linger (v) stay somewhere, possibly where you don't need to stay, or to stay for longer than necessary

manuscript (n) a writer's original pages of a book, article, or document before it is published

metaphysics (n) the part of philosophy that involves the study of ideas about life and existence

mock (adj) a mock feeling is one that you pretend you have, usually as a joke

moose (n) a large deer that lives in North America, northern Europe, and Asia

mumble (v) say something in a way that is not loud or clear enough so that your words are difficult to understand

obstinate (adj) difficult to remove, stubborn

orgy (n) a disorganized mixture

overwrought (adj) extremely emotional or upset

patent (adj) extremely obvious

perturbation (n) **perturbed** (adj) worried or upset by something

plod (v) walk with slow, heavy steps

precipitous (adj) very high and steep

purse your lips PHRASE press your lips together into a tight line

quaver (v) if your voice quavers, it is not steady because you are feeling emotional, nervous or afraid

rivet (v) attach with a metal clip

rooted to the spot PHRASE unable to move

scowl (v) twist your face into an expression that shows you are angry

sheer (adj) extremely steep

shrill (adj) a shrill noise or voice is very loud, high, and unpleasant

sonnet (n) a kind of poem

spasm (n) a sudden movement in your body caused when a muscle gets tight in a way you cannot control

squalor (n) poverty, used here to talk about the quality of Walt's poetry

sternness (n) a stern expression is serious and severe

stout (adj) very determined

strive (past **strove**) (v) try hard to do something

swish (n) the smooth gentle sound of something moving quickly through the air

tenderness (n) acting gently in a way that shows you care about someone

tentative (adj) not certain

too bad PHRASE used for saying that you are sorry or sympathetic about something

topaz (n) a clear yellow stone used for making jewellery

transmute (v) change metal into gold, used here to talk about how Walt makes money from his poems

vainly (adv) without success

vigorous (adj) full of energy

vouchsafe (v) admit

wheedle (v) try to persuade someone to do something by being intentionally charming

wilted (adj) if a plant wilts, it gradually bends towards the ground because it needs water, in the story Skiff Miller's collar is less stiff and upright than it should be

wry (adj) showing that you think something is funny but not very pleasant, often by the expression on your face

My Family and Other Animals

affronted (adj) insulted and angry

articulate (adj) clear and easy to understand

bark (n) the hard substance that covers a tree

beam (v) smile in a very obvious way

bemused (adj) confused

break off PHRASAL VERB stop doing something, especially speaking

brim (n) the part of a hat that sticks out from the base

brood (n) a group of young animals who all have the same mother and were born at the same time

bulge (v) be very full

burst its seams PHRASE be so full that the outside splits and what is inside comes out

by degrees PHRASE gradually

charcoal (n) a black substance made from burnt wood, used as a fuel, especially for cooking food

clingingly (adv) from verb **cling** stick to something very tightly

coax (v) gently persuade someone to do something

cobbles (n) small stones used in the past to make the surface of a road

commiseration (n) sympathy for someone who is unhappy about something

conducive (adj) creating a situation that helps something to happen

contemplate (v) think very carefully about something

coy (adj) someone who is coy pretends to be shy in order to make themselves seem more attractive

cravat (n) a wide piece of cloth that a man wears round his neck inside the collar of his shirt

delicacy (n) a rare or expensive type of food

doggedly (adv) from **dogged** (adj) determined to achieve something and continuing to try despite difficulties

drool (v) let saliva (the liquid in your mouth) come out of your mouth

dupe (v) trick someone into believing something that is not true

eccentricities (n) ideas, actions, or habits that are strange or unusual

encrusted (adj) covered with a hard layer of something

exuberance (n) a state of energetic happiness and excitement

fling (v) (past **flung**) move your body or part of your body quickly, and with a lot of force

gesticulate (v) make movements with your hands and arms when you are talking

get/gain a purchase PHRASE get a firm hold on something

gruffly (adv) in a voice that has a rough low sound

heartrending (adj) making you feel very sad and sympathetic

hedge (n) a line of bushes or small trees growing close together around a garden or field

hue (n) a colour or shade

implacable (adj) having very determined feelings that will not change

imploringly (adv) asking someone to do something in a way that shows that you want them to do it very much

in a daze PHRASE not concentrating, thinking clearly, or understanding what is happening around you

ingratiating (adj) done in an attempt to get someone's approval

ivory (n) the bone that an elephant's tusks are made of

jig (n) a fast traditional dance that involves a lot of small jumping steps

mar (v) spoil something

martyred look PHRASE look at someone with an expression that shows them you are suffering

menagerie (n) a large collection of wild animals kept in captivity (i.e. in cages)

merry-go-round (n) a machine with models of animals or vehicles that children ride on as it goes round in a circle

mutter (v) talk in a quiet voice that is difficult to hear, especially because you are talking to yourself

obese (adj) too fat, in a way that is dangerous for your health

pantomime (n) a play performed using only the movements of your body and face to tell a story or express yourself

peel off (v) remove the skin from something, e.g. fruit

peevishly (adv) from **peevish** (adj) easily annoyed, especially by things that are not important

peroxide (v) turn your hair blonde by using a chemical called peroxide

pleadingly (adv) if you look at someone pleadingly, your expression shows that you want something very much

ply with PHRASAL VERB keep giving someone a lot of presents, food, or drinks

pollen (n) a powder produced by flowers. It is carried by the wind or insects to other flowers so that they can produce new seeds

pompom, or **pompon** (n) a ball made of wool or feathers, used as a decoration on clothing

pore over PHRASAL VERB examine something very carefully

pout out PHRASAL VERB if you pout out your chest or lips, you push them out further than normal

precariously (adv) not safely, likely to fall

prune (v) remove parts of a plant, for example, to make it grow better

regally (adv) like a king or queen

rivalry (n) a situation in which people (or animals) compete with one another

rustling (n) the sound that papers or leaves make when they are moved

screw up your face PHRASE pull your forehead down and push your mouth and nose up

scrutiny (n) careful examination of someone or something

secluded (adj) private, peaceful, and not near other people or places

sentimentalism (n) a tendency to express sadness, sympathy, love, etc in a way that seems excessive

sentry (n) a soldier who stands at the entrance to a place and guards it

serge (n) a strong thick cloth made from wool

sleek (adj) sleek fur or hair is smooth and shiny

sneeringly (adv) in an unpleasant way that shows you do not respect someone

sprightly (adj) healthy and with a lot of energy

stilts (n) long narrow structures used to raise something above the ground

stumble across/on/upon PHRASAL VERB find something, or to meet someone, by accident

sullen (adj) showing that you are in an unhappy mood, and do not want to communicate

surge (v) move forwards very quickly

take your fancy PHRASE start to want to have, or something that appeals to you

tar (n) a thick black liquid made from coal, used especially for making the surfaces of roads

tinge (n) a small amount of a colour, feeling, or quality

totter (v) stand in a way that is not steady

tumble (v) move in a disorganized way

unorthodox (adj) not following the usual or traditional rules. This could apply to religion, society, etc

verve (n) energy and enthusiasm

wag (v) if a dog wags its tail, it moves its tail from one side to the other several times

weed (v) remove plants that you do not want

Language study index

The Cat that Walked by Himself

Uses of *so*
Linkers

The Princess and the Puma

Talking about the past – modal verbs and the perfect infinitive
Verb patterns

The Grey Parrot

Present and perfect participle clauses
Idiomatic expressions

Lappin and Lapinova

Ellipsis
Discourse markers

Brown Wolf

Fronting
Common expressions

My Family and Other Animals

Would for past habits
Multiple-clause sentences

Visit the Macmillan Readers website at
www.macmillanenglish.com/readers

*to find **FREE resources** for use in class and for independent learning. Search our **online catalogue** to buy new Readers including **audio download** and **eBook** versions.*

Here's a taste of what's available:

For the classroom:

- **Tests** for most Readers to check understanding and monitor progress
- **Worksheets** for most Readers to explore language and themes
- **Listening worksheets** to practise extensive listening
- Worksheets to help prepare for the **First (FCE) reading exam**

Additional resources for students and independent learners:

- An **online level test** to identify reading level
- **Author information sheets** to provide in-depth biographical information about our Readers authors
- **Self-study worksheets** to help track and record your reading which can be used with any Reader
- Use our **creative writing worksheets** to help you write short stories, poetry and biographies
- Write academic essays and literary criticism confidently with the help of our **academic writing worksheets**
- Have fun completing our **webquests** and **projects** and learn more about the Reader you are studying
- Go backstage and read **interviews** with **famous authors** and **actors**
- Discuss your favourite Readers at the **Book Corner Club**

*Visit www.macmillanenglish.com/readers **to find out more!***